BUILDING A GAS FIRED CRUCIBLE FURNACE

Written & Illustrated

By

DAVID J. GINGERY

printed in U.S.A.

LIBRARY OF CONGRESS CATALOG

CARD NUMBER 88-91058

INTERNATIONAL STANDARD

BOOK NUMBER 0-9604330-7-4

DAVID J. GINGERY

SPRINGFIELD, MO

CONTENTS

INTRODUCTION

The melting furnace and methods described in this manual are the product of several years of research and experimentation. The objective was to design a unit that could be built and operated in the home shop to melt as much as 20 pounds of grey iron, and of course an equal volume of aluminum, brass or any other alloy of lower temperature requirement. The final product exceeds all original expectations and it is both easy and inexpensive to build.

While the primary stated objective was to develop an iron melting furnace, it was no great surprise to find that the mere melting of iron does not ensure a supply of useable iron castings for projects. There are technical problems with grey iron casting beyond the high temperature required. Never-the-less we now have the capability to melt the iron and with determination we can work through the remaining problems. These are primarily slag removal and maintaining the required carbon and silicon content.

I still feel that the simple solid fuel furnace is the best choice for the absolute novice and for those who will continue to produce only a few castings occasionally. It is easier to build and operate, and aluminum or zinc alloys are far easier to work with than iron or brass. There are really very few instances in the home shop where aluminum or zinc alloy would not be entirely practical in place of iron. And there are instances when they might actually be superior to iron though not practical at the commercial level. But those who begin as novices acquire skill and many will look for a greater challenge. And there are instances when only a grey iron casting will do.

To melt iron or brass is not the only reason to consider up-grading the shop. If a greater volume of work is to be done efficiently and economically it makes plenty of sense to build a gas fired crucible furnace. And of course gas is cleaner than charcoal or coke as well as more convenient. My only objection to using the higher temperature metals always has been, and remains, the great danger of handling molten metal at temperatures up to and above 2800 degrees F. Yet it is quite easily within the ability of a home foundry provided that you proceed with careful planning and great caution. A 20 pound charge of molten iron or brass is at least twice as dangerous as the same volume of aluminum or zinc alloy and it is no casual matter to handle.

Without doubt gas, either natural or propane, is the most practical, efficient and economical fuel commonly available to home shop operators. While it is true that in order to achieve the high temperature required to produce metal castings you must burn an explosive mixture, that does not mean you are building a bomb. But you must realize that there is an explosion hazzard among other dangers. Understanding that a cooking range, home furnace or water heater also burns an explosive mixture should calm your nerves but not make you complacent, or worse, CARELESS.

Now an explosion might be merely a "pop" or a "whoosh". Or it might be a great "whoomph" or a "kablooie". It depends upon the volume of explosive mixture of gas and air confined at the moment of ignition. Consequences can range from a mild fright with singed eyebrows to total destruction of property and severe injury to persons or even death. Your objective is to never allow any amount of explosive mixture to accumulate. That is not difficult but it does require cautious planning and attention to detail.

There are some major differences between domestic gas appliances and the burner that is used in this particular melting furnace. First, this is a forced draft burner while most domestic appliances use an atmospheric burner, which is generally some form of a bunsen burner. We burn a greater volume of gas in a confined space in less time and so temperature is much higher. The other important difference is that domestic appliances have a number of so called 'safety controls' that are designed to shut off the gas supply in the event of ignition failure or other disfunction. These devices are tested on each specific application to absolutely ensure that they work under all operating conditions. It would require a manual larger than this to begin to describe the tests alone and so no attempt is made to do so. There is nothing automatic about this home built burner. It is lighted and extinguished manually and you must personally attend it all the time it is operating. While there are many devices available that might be installed on a home built burner, none of them can truly be called 'safety controls' until they have been very thoroughly tested under conditions not easily achieved in the home shop. Presumption of safety when it is not absolutely proven is the most dangerous condition of all.

On this particular burner the only suggested auxilliary control is a line voltage solenoid valve that is installed to shut off the gas supply in the event of a power failure. This is a rather important feature since the furnace might be quite unapproachable if the forced draft is suddenly lost. But you still must be on hand to shut off the manual valve and the fan switch since the solenoid valve would naturally open and admit gas if power is restored. It would be a serious error to presume that this device provides more safety protection than it actually does and this example is sited to inspire you to give the most careful thought to any modifications you make to the design. I don't mean at all to discourage you from upgrading your furnace by the addition of safety devices. That will be the best of good ideas. But

I stress that this aspect of furnace building will not tolerate a casual or careless approach.

There are many dangers inherent in foundry work other than explosion and no attempt is made in this manual to list them all, or even a majority of them. It would require a rather large book to list the many potential dangers and the precautiions that might be followed to avoid them. But that would make for dismal reading and would serve no useful purpose. The intention here is to describe a furnace project that will expand the capacity of a small shop. With reasonable caution a practical gas fired melting furnace can be built and operated without disaster. The key to safety lies in your careful attention to every detail of construction and, more important, of the operation of your foundry when it is complete.

Since "Charcoal Foundry" was published about 10 years ago thousands have discovered the many advantages of adding a simple foundry to the home shop operation. To be able to produce your own castings for parts, working stock and other ornamental shapes adds so much to the total shop experience. And it reduces operating cost greatly as compared to purchasing such items if they actually happen to be available. Many have asked for means to expand their operation to both greater volume and higher melting temperature. There has been much interest expressed in casting grey iron as well as brass and bronze and so this manual is my response.

CHAPTER I
THE BASIC DESIGN

While there are many details in the construction of a gas fired furnace, the principles are very easily understood. No great amount of mechanical skill is required and the needed materials are easily found in most parts of the modern world. This particular design was developed by an amateur for amateurs and it has some features that make it appropriate for the home shop or other small shop where funds available for such equipment might be limited.

The materials called out are generally light in weight and of a common nature so that costs can be kept to an absolute minimum. Certainly heavier materials can be used if they are available except where dimension is vital. The home blended refractory liner proves quite durable but of course the commercial castable refractories are superior in many ways though quite costly.

Much of the construction is by welding and so all of the appropriate safety precautions should be followed. Galvanized, zinc dipped or other plated metal should not be welded due to very hazardous fumes. While galvanized metal was used for the original test models of this furnace that is not the recommended material since it is possible that skin temperatures could get high enough to vaporize the zinc. Common black sheet iron is the best material to use for the outer skin of the furnace sections, but galvanized sheet metal is OK for the blower assembly. The remainder of the construction materials are common angle iron, strap iron, pipe and fittings and standard hardware and fasteners. Much of it may already be on hand in many shops. Only basic tools will be required and these include of course an arc welder and some source of heat for brazing such as a torch or carbon arc. A hacksaw, drill, snips, blind rivet tool, hammer and other light hand tools will do the remainder of the job.

The entire unit is a composite of parts and assemblies which includes the frame with its mechanisms, the furnace body and the fan/burner. All of these except the fan/burner are seen in figures 1, 2 and 3. We can begin with a discussion of these parts and assemblies and you will see that the names are self defining.

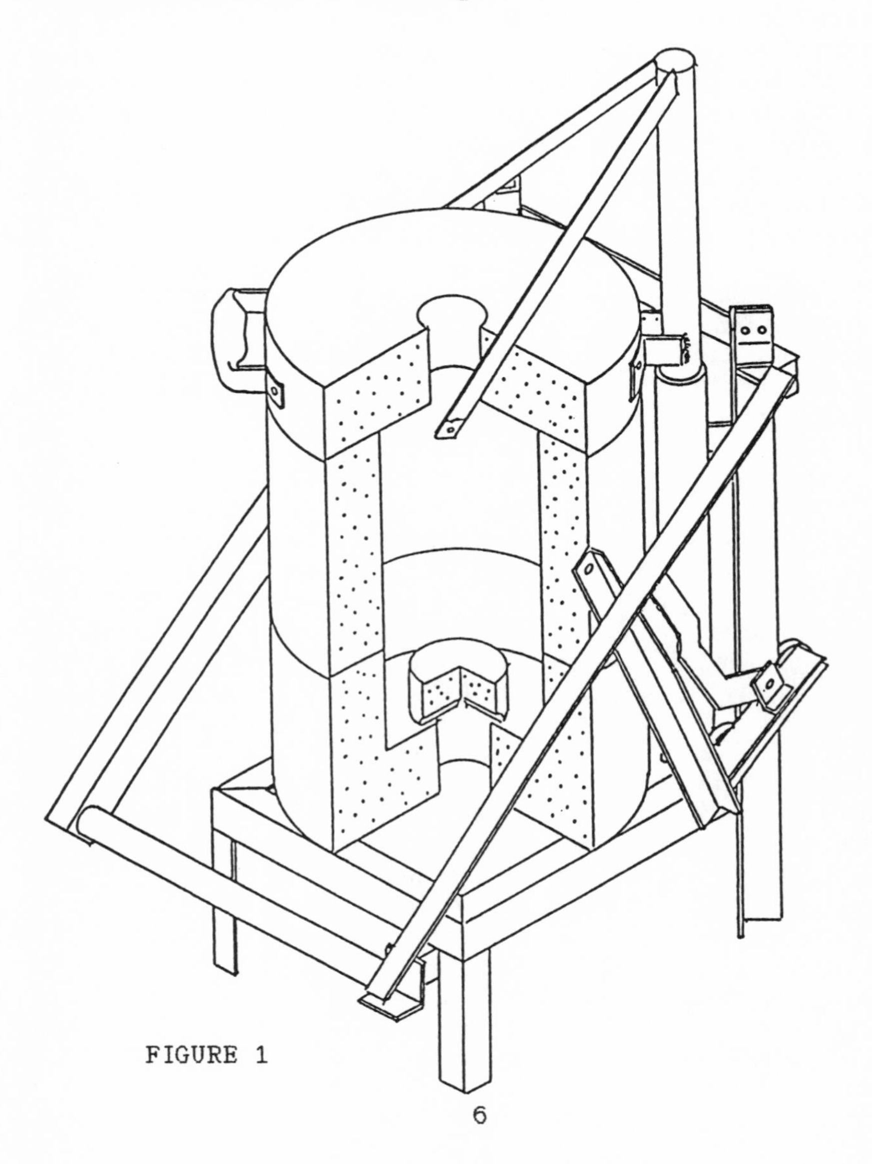

FIGURE 1

Notice in figure 1 that the furnace body is made up in four parts which are the base, the central body, the lid and the 'plinth' (crucible block). The base rests permanently on the frame while the central body and lid can be raised for access to the crucible and to light the fire. you will see also the pedal that raises the lid so that it can be swung aside, and the mechanism for raising the central body.

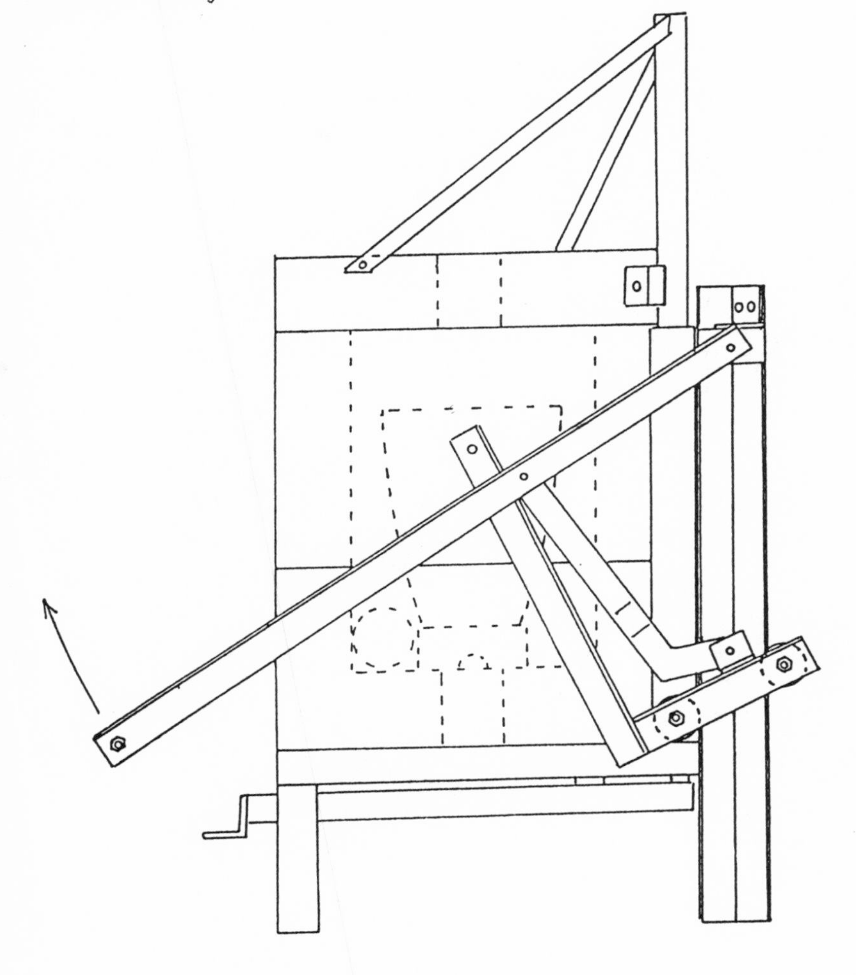

figure 2

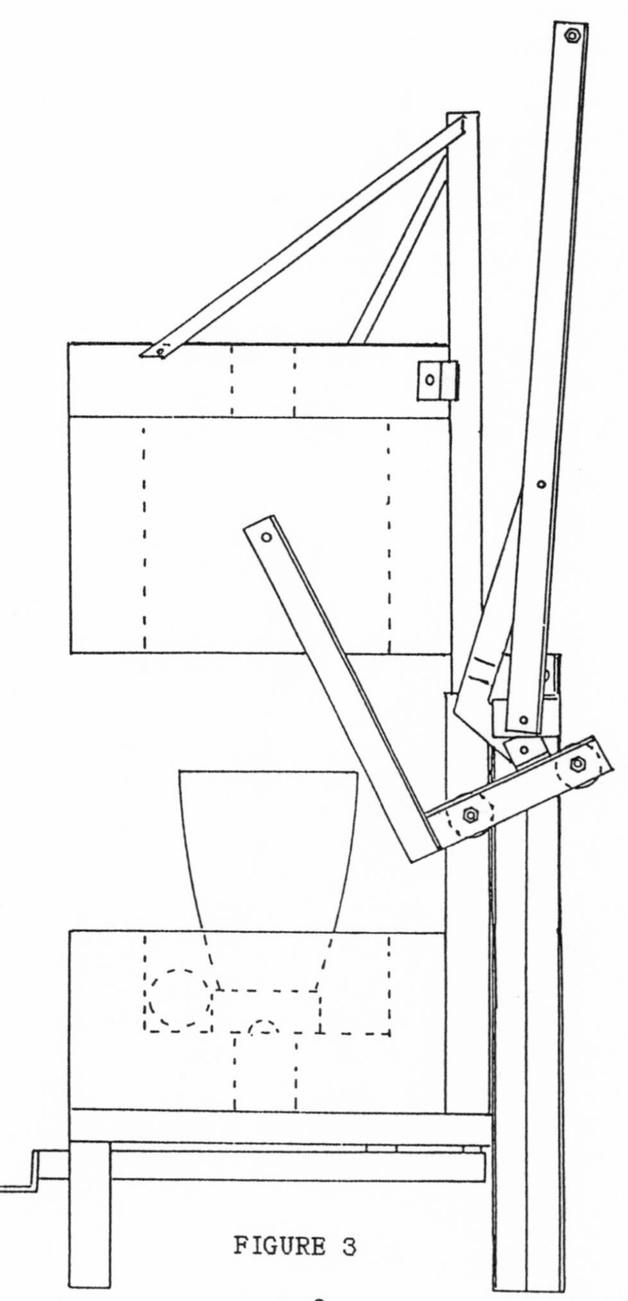

FIGURE 3

Figure 2 shows the furnace in its normal operating position with a crucible resting on the plinth. The dotted circle to the left of the plinth is the burner inlet. There is a 'safety hole' in the bottom of the base and grooves in the bottom of the plinth so that molten metal will drain out in the event that a crucible breaks or spills. There is a clear view of the foot pedal that raises the lid and the mechanism for raising the central body. The arrow at the lifting handle indicates the direction of action.

In figure 3 you see the handle raised and both the central body and lid have followed. The central body is fastened to the lifting arms with two studs and the lid lifting mechanism telescopes to allow the body to raise.

Figure 4 shows the entire frame with the lid lifting mechanism added. This is all a very simple weldment of angle iron, strap iron and standard pipe. In figure 5 the lifting mechanism for the central body has been added to give you a clear view of the ball bearing rollers that ride the vertical track of the frame. Two lifting arms, two links and two levers raise the body with a two to one mechanical advantage. A length of standard pipe joins the two levers to give one hand operation. The furnace sections rest on the frame and the lid brackets are welded to the lid standard to complete the assembly.

Figure 6 shows an internal view of the fan/burner assembly. This is a simple centrifugal fan driven by a fractional horse power electric motor through a belt drive. A simple shutter is used at the inlet of the fan to regulate the volume of air. There is an orfice brazed inside the burner delivery tube that creates a partial vacuum at the gas inlet, which is merely a half pipe nipple brazed to the tube. A manual valve regulates the volume of gas.

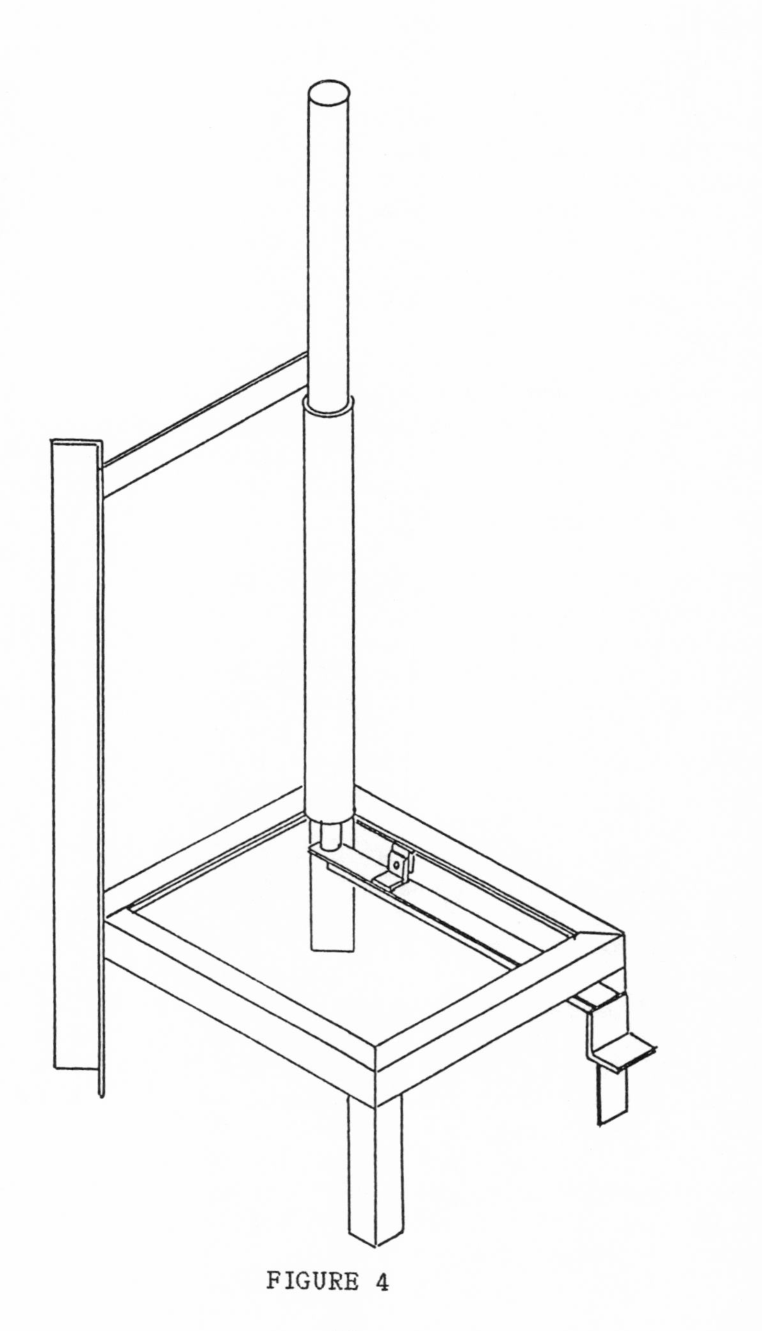

FIGURE 4

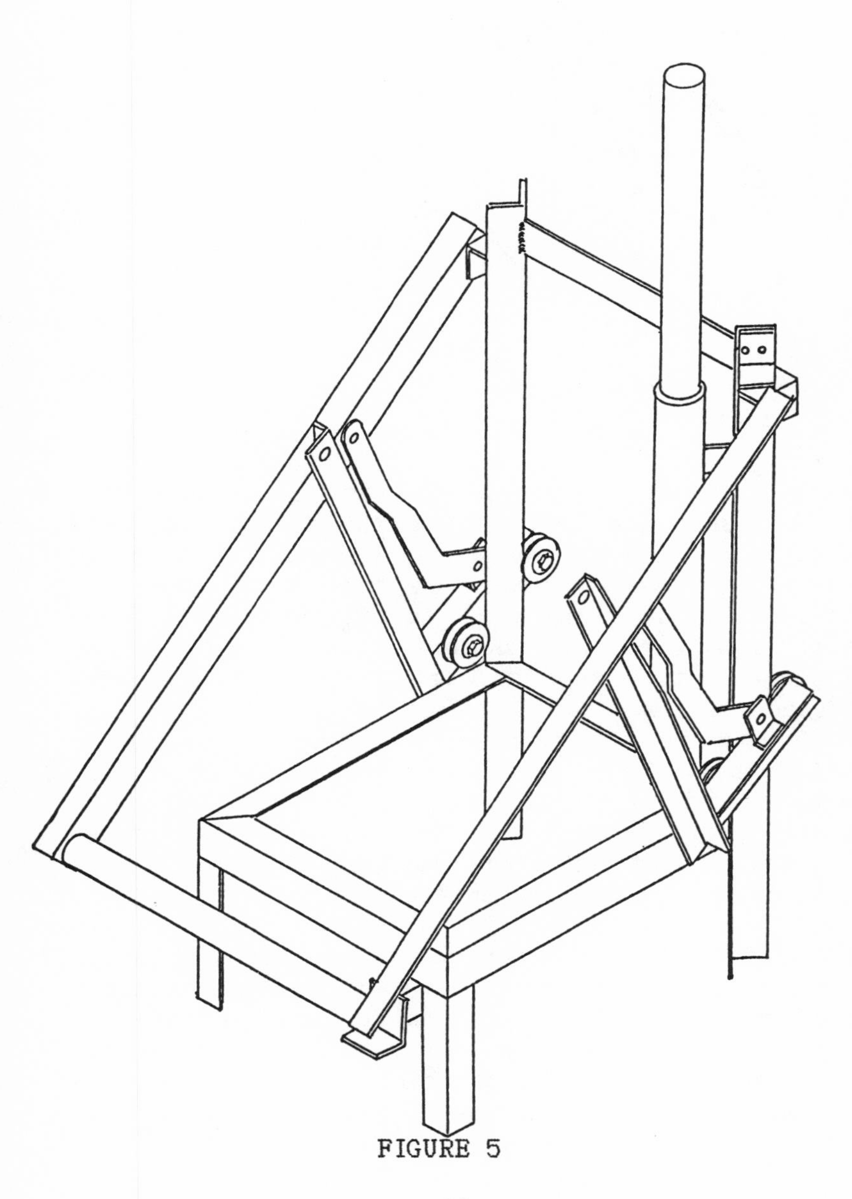

FIGURE 5

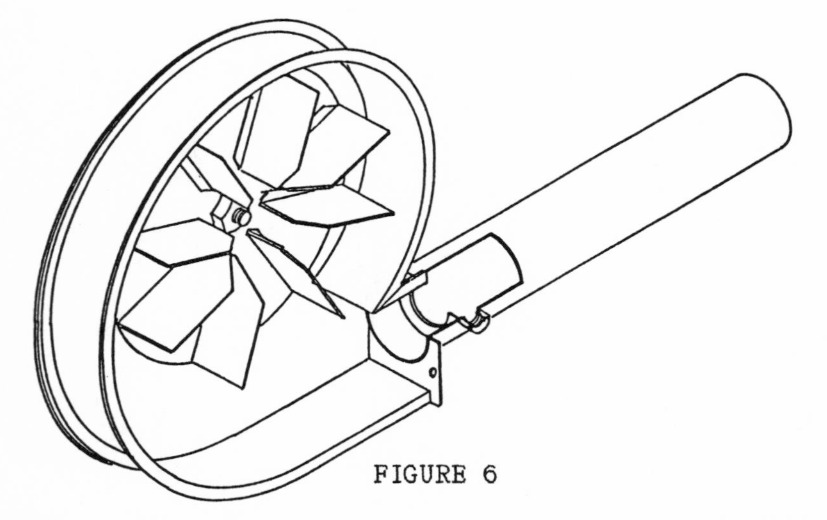

FIGURE 6

It is true that a simpler furnace can be built to do the same job but each of the features of this unit offers some advantage. The ability to raise the body makes lighting the fire much safer and easier than reaching down inside the body. It is also much safer and easier to grasp the crucible from the side than it is to lift it from the furnace and set it in a pouring shank. This is much more important if you will melt iron or brass since the radiant heat is much more intense than with aluminum or zinc alloy. Likewise, it is a great advantage to swing the lid aside rather than to lift it off or hinge it back, for its inside surface will radiate intense heat.

I've termed this burner an 'after-mix' burner to distinguish it from the common 'pre-mix' burner used commercially. The term 'pre-mix' means that the gas enters the fan inlet, and mixing of gas and air takes place in the blower housing. In this design the gas enters the delivery tube 'after' the fan.

I have little doubt but that the pre-mix design is superior but I don't believe that the advantage is significant enough to matter in this application. The fan housing must be absolutely air tight at its periphery if you pre-mix and that adds much work to the fabrication of the housing. The simple orfice in the delivery tube makes it possible to achieve nearly the same results with less cost and labor. If you elect to experiment with the pre-mix design then of course the orfice should be eliminated.

You may be tempted to use available air from a vacuum cleaner rather than to build the fan detailed here. But there are at least three good reasons to reconsider. First, some vacuum cleaners draw air over the motor windings and commutator brushes so there is danger of carrying sparks in the air stream that could ignite the gas mixture in the tube. Second, it is neccessary to restrict the airflow to adjust flame size and that can be harmful to some types of vacuum cleaners. Specifically, canister types and some cheaper shop vacuums use the main air stream to cool the motor. Finally, the high noise level of a vacuum cleaner can be distracting and itself a hazard in the shop. There are some of the older upright vacuums with a motor/blower unit that can be nicely adapted to burner use if you don't object to the noise. The fan detailed in this manual is not difficult to build and it is ideally suited to the job at hand. What is generally most appreciated about this burner is its low noise level in both the fan and the combustion chamber. This is because we use a large diameter wheel at lower speed, and the delivery tube is larger than common practice to give lower velocity. The combined result is intense flame right at the base of the crucible and lower noise level.

This unit can be used effectively for a wide range of melting and casting jobs including some metallurgical operations. While it is quite small it is really as large as any one amateur should try to handle. At least until considerable experience has been gained. 20 pounds of molten iron or brass in a number 8 crucible is an awesome thing to behold for the first time. It requires some knowledge, skill and considerable physical strength to safely and successfully deliver the molten charge to its appointed destination.

While the chamber is large enough to contain a number 10 crucible the intended capacity is a number 8 crucible. That would contain about 8 pounds of molten aluminum or something in excess of 20 pounds of molten brass or grey iron. Of course smaller crucibles can be used as well. Zinc alloys melt at temperatures under 1000 degrees F. while aluminum pours at about 1400 degrees F. Brass pours at near 2000 degrees F. and grey iron at near 2800 degrees F.. This furnace will melt all of them but of course the higher melting range takes longer. A 20 pound charge of grey iron can take 45 minutes or longer from a cold start while a full pot of zinc alloy or alluminum can be had in just a short time. Your inititial melts should be significantly less than maximum capacity until you have gained sufficient skill and confidence to handle more.

There have been no long term tests made of this unit and so you should carefully examine all parts frequently for any signs of stress or failure. Stress cracks, failing welds, rivets or screws loosening or deteriorating refractory are all very clear warnings that repairs are in order. There is a tendency to think that because there have been no disasters after repeated use that there will be no disasters in the immediate future. The notion is unsound and you must not presume you are safe. Any attempt to increase the size and capacity of this design should be preceded by a careful study of all aspects. Especially of the matter of handling the larger melts, such as two man shanks, mechanical aids to lift the crucible from the furnace and increased gas and power requirement.

The author of this manual is an amateur and you must realize the limitations of my knowledge and experience. Each detail presented here is subject to your own appraisal and you are fully responsible for your own safety and that of any others who might be injured due to your pursuit of this activity.

CHAPTER II
BUILDING THE FURNACE BODY

SELECT THE LINING MATERIAL

There are two main options in the lining material for the furnace: A commercially prepared castable refractory or a home blended lining. Local availability will be the main factor in the decision since buying such a bulky product by mail order is usually not practical. If you live in a small rural community it is likely that you will have to travel to the nearest larger city or industrial center to get at least some of the materials you need.

A COMMERCIALLY PREPARED LINING

Without doubt the most convenient material to use for the refractory lining would be one of the many forms of "dry-mix castable refractory". There are many companies who offer them and there is a wide variety of types for many industrial applications. Some are so exotic and expensive that they are out of the question for most of us in the home shop. But a very few will meet our needs and be affordable to some.

These products are actually a sort of refractory concrete. That is they cure chemically, like concrete, to a rock-hard mass. They are blends of clay, aggregate and phosphoric acid. They are sometimes termed 'phosphate bonded'. Sometimes available in 50 pound bags but more often only in 100 pound bags. There are some refractory blends that are put up moist and ready to use but these are generally very costly and not the best choice for this application. You want a 'dry-mix castable refractory' that is rated for 2800 degrees F. or higher.

Now the highest temperature ratings are more costly and you don't want to go to extremes. So try to find one that is as near to the rating as possible. Inquire at industrial supply, building supply, masonry supply such as brick and concrete block companies, fireplace, stove and furnace supply and those who supply to the ceramics hobbiest. It may require a dilligent search but you should be able to turn up several sources. By all means shop around because there is a very wide range of prices for these materials. Be prepared to spend some extra time searching if you resolve to use a commercial castable refractory, but the time will be well spent.

Directions for mixing and use will come with the product you buy. In general you can mix it with a hoe or a trowel just as you would mortar, but you will use less water than is used in mortar. The moistened mix is tamped into the forms rather than pouring it in and so a minimum of water is used. Excess water tends to reduce the final strength so you must mix with care. These products set chemically to a rock hard mass like concrete but they do not set up as fast as concrete. They do not have to be fired to harden them as with the home brewed mix but they will vitrify when fired. The usual rule is to gradually increase the temperature on the first use until a bright red heat is reached. Then you can rapidly raise the temperature as high as you like. Be sure to follow any special instructions for your product. These products are not mixed or moistened until you are ready to use them and the open working time is usually less than one hour. Once moistened they will set up chemically and they can't be made plastic again. And they must be allowed to stand for a number of hours before they can be handled. The usual rule is over night.

A HOME BLEND LINING

There is no need to give up if you can't find a commercial castable refractory or if the cost is too high for a limited shop budget. A home brewed lining will serve very well and it will be significantly cheaper. The main ingredients are clay, sand, 'grog' and water. Again, you might have to hunt a little for the fire clay. The logical sources are the same as those for the castable refractory. It is possible that the sub-soil in your area contains enough clay to make a satisfactory lining. Just sift out rocks, trash and organic material through a window screen, moisten and form into a brick and fire to a red heat with a charcoal fire. If it will form a firm cake when slightly moist and fuse into a permanently hard brick when fired it will probably make a satisfactory furnace lining. There are ways to improve the quality of the material if it is not satisfactory at first.

A blend of two parts silica sand and one part fire clay is the very old tested and proven formula used for patching furnace linings. You can make a lining of this alone but it will certainly shrink and crack drastically when it is fired.

You can replace up to one half of the silica sand with 'grog'. This is merely some form of burned clay. Some smashed up fire brick will make excellent grog and the brick yard may be willing to let you have some broken bricks at little or no cost. Insulating fire bricks are soft and easily broken up while hard bricks require considerable effort to pulverize them. Nearly any kind of bricks will do for this application, but old mortar should be cleaned off because the lime is not desireable in the furnace lining. Be certain to wear eye protection when you break up bricks. This can be tedious work but the improvement of the lining is so great that it is worth it. I used a two pound hammer and simply kept breaking the pieces ever smaller until it resembled very course sand.

The grog is the ingredient that reduces or eliminates shrinking and the silica sand tends to reduce expansion at high temperatures. The fire clay is the binder and the water makes it all workable so that it can be molded into the desired shape.

Old timers added common salt or borax up to 10%, or a blend of both salt and borax to the cupola patch. This forms a hard glaze on the surface when the lining is fired but it will burn away in time. In my experience the borax seems to improve the wet strength of the blend to help hold it together until it is fully vitrified by firing. I no longer use salt.

It is very important to mix all of the ingredients thoroughly while dry. They simply will not blend well when wet and the lining will fail. Water is to be sprinkled over the dry-mixed ingredients and mixing is continuous as water is added. The objective is to achieve a coarse, grainy, plastic mass that can be formed into a very firm cake. If you squeeze a handful into a ball it can be broken in half cleanly as shown in figure 7. It will resemble mortar that does not have enough water in it. If it is 'soupy' it will sag in the forms and give you much trouble. If you accidentally get it too wet you can add more blended dry material to get it into proper 'ramming shape'. When it is uniformly moist it should be covered with a damp cloth or plastic and allowed to stand for at least several hours before use. It takes some length of time for the clay to become fully plastic and cohesive and the quality of the material will improve greatly if allowed to stand over night before use. It will keep indefinitly in a sealed container such as a plastic bag or pail with a tight fitting lid. If you elect the home-brewed refractory it will be best to mix it up in advance of building the forms so it will be ready for use when you want it. The quality of this material will actually improve with age as long as it is not allowed to dry out so there is no need to hurry the project.

FIGURE 7

A GOOD FORMULA

4 gallons of silica sand
4 gallons of grog
4 gallons of fire clay
3 quarts of borax powder

The above quantity will be enough to complete the furnace as detailed here and some will be left over for possible later repairs if needed.

THE OUTER FORMS

Each of the forms except that of the plinth is a simple sheet metal cylinder that becomes the permanent outer skin of the furnace body. Galvanized iron as light as 30 gauge was used on one of the early test models. Although it seemed durable enough a heavier weight will be better. There is a definite danger that the skin temperature can get high enough to vaporize zinc during use and so galvanized metal is not recommended for this application. 26 gauge black iron is suggested for all of the forms. Of course you can use heavier metal if you are able to cut it and form it. You might want to consider buying your sheet metal sheared to size at a local sheet metal shop if you do not have a good, hefty pair of snips. You might also want to have the cylinders rolled up if you choose a heavier weight metal. Three forms will be needed. One each for the base, the central body and the lid. An additional piece of light gauge metal will be needed for the temporary internal form and that can be 30 gauge galvanized since it will not be exposed to the fire.

The length of the metal for the forms is the circumfrence of the 13" outer diameter plus an allowance for the seam. And so 13" X 3.1416 = 40.8408". You can round it off to 41" for convenience since the actual figure is very near to

40 7/8". Add 3/8" to each end for the lap to give a total length of 41 3/4".

Each of the forms is of the same length but they differ in height and other details. Figure 8 represents one half of each form layout and the shear size for each piece of sheet metal is given.

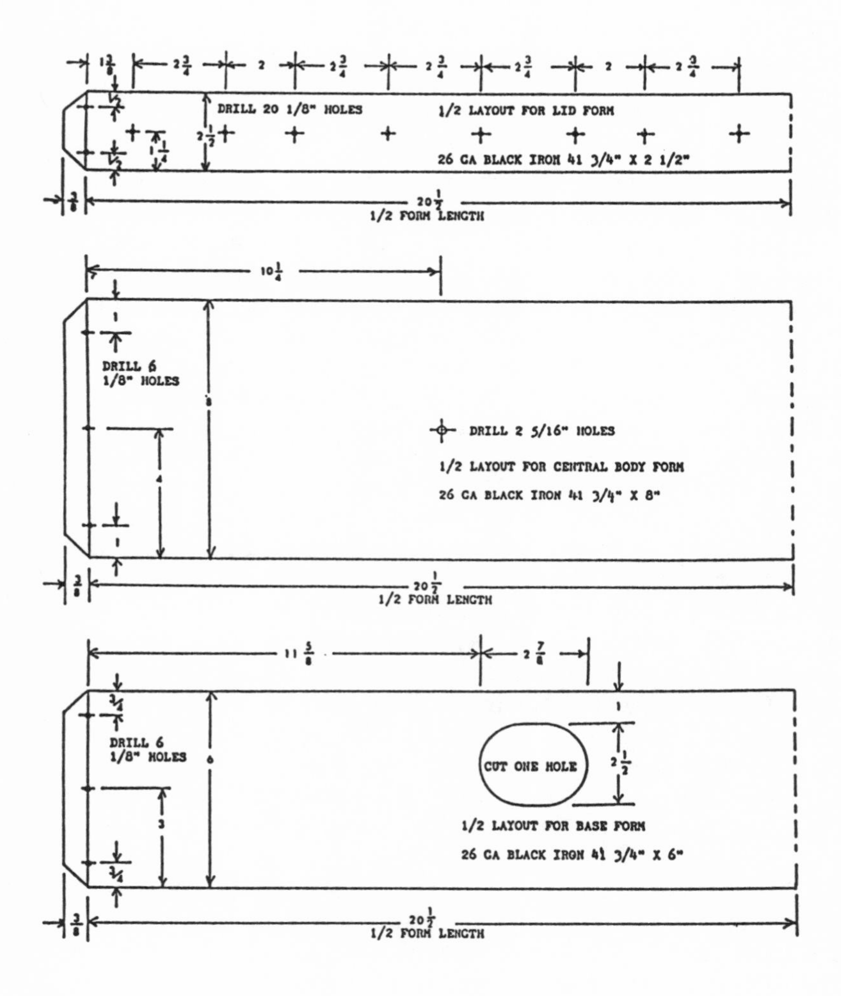

FIGURE 8

The lid and the central body are fully symmetrical and so the opposite end layout is identical. But the base differs in that only one half has the hole for the burner tube inlet. Make one each of these forms, roll them up and join them at the seams with rivets, sheet metal screws or machine screws and nuts.

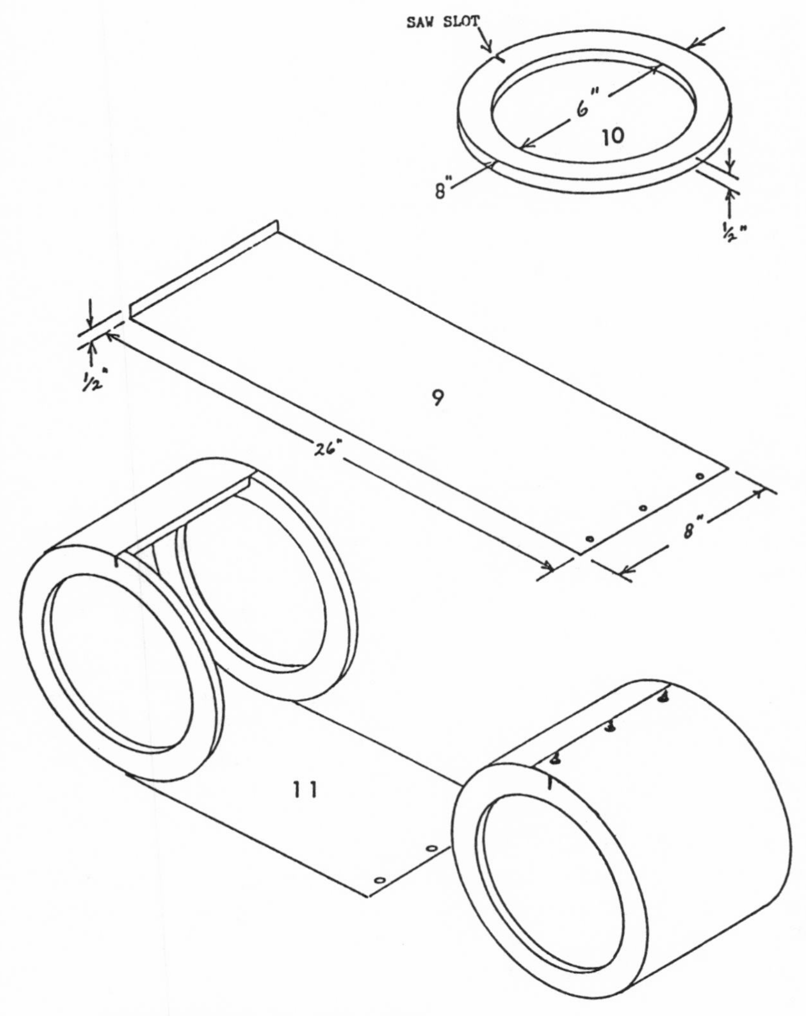

TEMPORARY INSIDE FORM

TNE INSIDE FORM

Both the base and the central body have an inside diameter of 8" and so we need a temporary collapsible form. 30 gauge galvanized iron will be OK for this form. Shear it to 26 1/2" X 8" with three 1/8" holes drilled near one end and a 1/2" flange bent at right angles on the other end as shown in figure 9. A pair of 8" diameter discs with a 6" diameter hole in the center of each one can be cut from 1/2" plywood. (figure 10) Just slip the flange into the saw slots and roll up the form as shown in figure 11. Secure the end temporarily with tape as you drill the three holes through. Then install three #8 X 1/2" sheet metal screws from the inside so that they can be removed to collapse the form later.

THE BURNER INLET FORM

The flame is made to enter the combustion chamber at a tangent so that it will swirl around the base of the crucible so the inlet fitting is just a little bit more complex than a simple tube. While you could gradually cut the end of a length of tubing to fit by trial and error that would be a tedious job. This is the best of all times to learn how to lay out a cylinder intersection in case you don't already know how to do that.

The layout process is called 'Parallel line development' and it is easy and pleasant work. We begin with a full sized plan view, which shows the combustion chamber and the burner inlet tube as they appear looking down at the top of the base section. It is not neccessary to show the entire combustion chamber but only that portion where the inlet tube intersects as you see in figure 12. The inlet tube will be 3" long at its shortest dimension so that it will protrude beyond the outer shell.

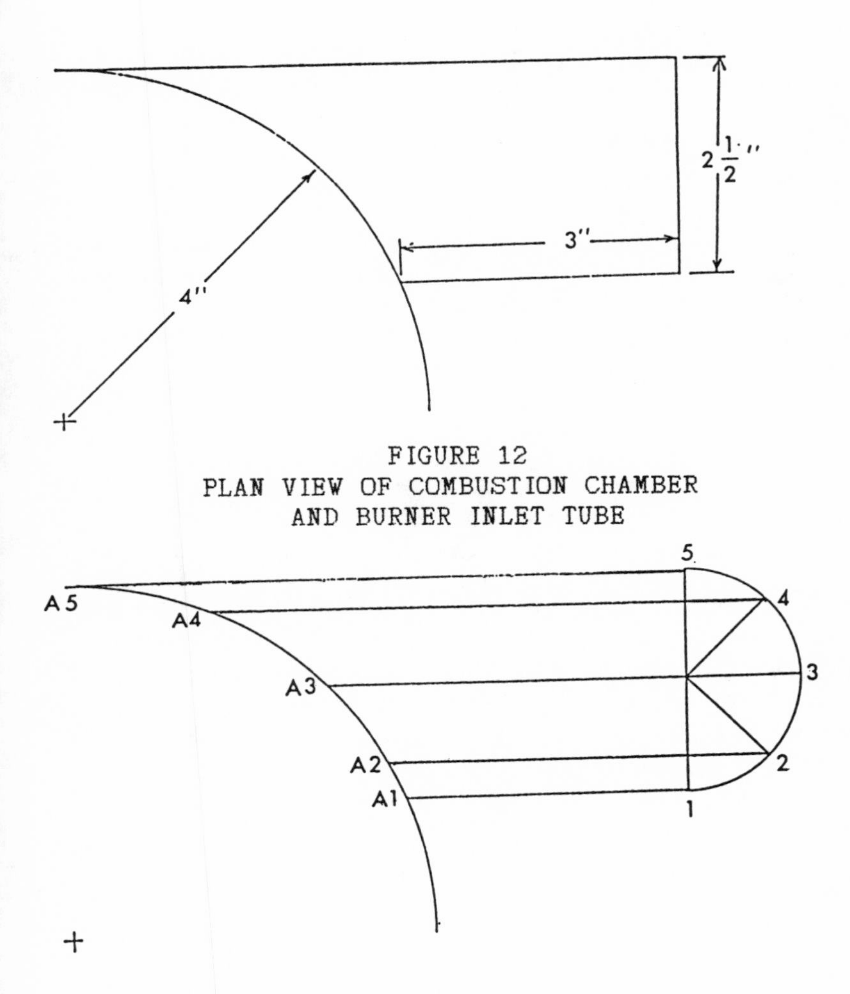

FIGURE 12
PLAN VIEW OF COMBUSTION CHAMBER
AND BURNER INLET TUBE

FIGURE 13

Draw one half of a 2 1/2" diameter circle at the end of the inlet tube and divide the half circle into four equal parts. Number each point of intersection from 1 through 5 as shown in figure 13. Extend five horizontal lines from each point of intersection to intersect with the 8" diameter circle and number them A-1 through A-5.

Extend a vertical line to represent the the outside end of the inlet tube. determine the distance between points 1 and 2 on the 2 1/2" circle and mark off four equal spaces of that dimension on the vertical line. Number the points of intersection 1-B through 5-B. Extend horizontal 'parallel' lines from each point of intersection as in figure 14.

Now extend vertical 'parallel' lines from points 1-A through 5-A to intersect with the horizontal 'parallel' lines 1-B through 5-B. By now there is no need to explain why the process is named as it is. The intersections establish points 1-A-B through 5-A-B and you have what is called the 'stretchout' of one half of the pattern.

The layout work can be done directly on sheet metal but it is usually easier and more accurate to do it on heavy paper or light bristol. Then you lay the half pattern stretchout over sheet metal and make a prick punch at each point of intersection. Add an amount for the lap seam and punch a pair of hole centers where you will join it together. The center of the joint is on line 1-A-B. Cutting out the half pattern is merely a game of 'connect-the-dot'. Trace the pattern twice on your sheet metal stock and you have the full layout as shown in figure 16. Make only one burner inlet tube.

The whole process takes far less time than it does to explain it. Once mastered this simple skill will serve you on many future jobs.

THE VENT AND SAFETY HOLE FORMS

The vent hole in the lid is 2 1/2" diameter and so a cylinder 2 1/2" in diameter and 2 1/2" long will serve to form the opening. The safety hole in the base is 2" in diameter so you need a 2 1/2" length of 2" tubing.

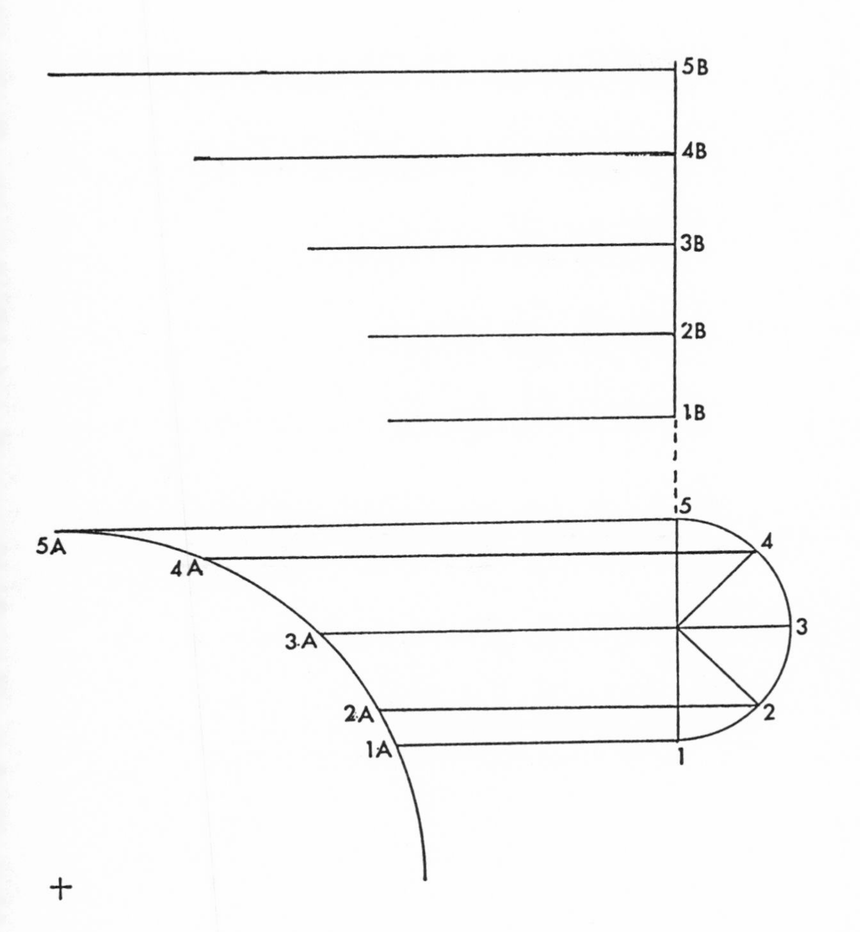

FIGURE 14

EXTEND VERTICAL LINE AND PARALLEL LINES

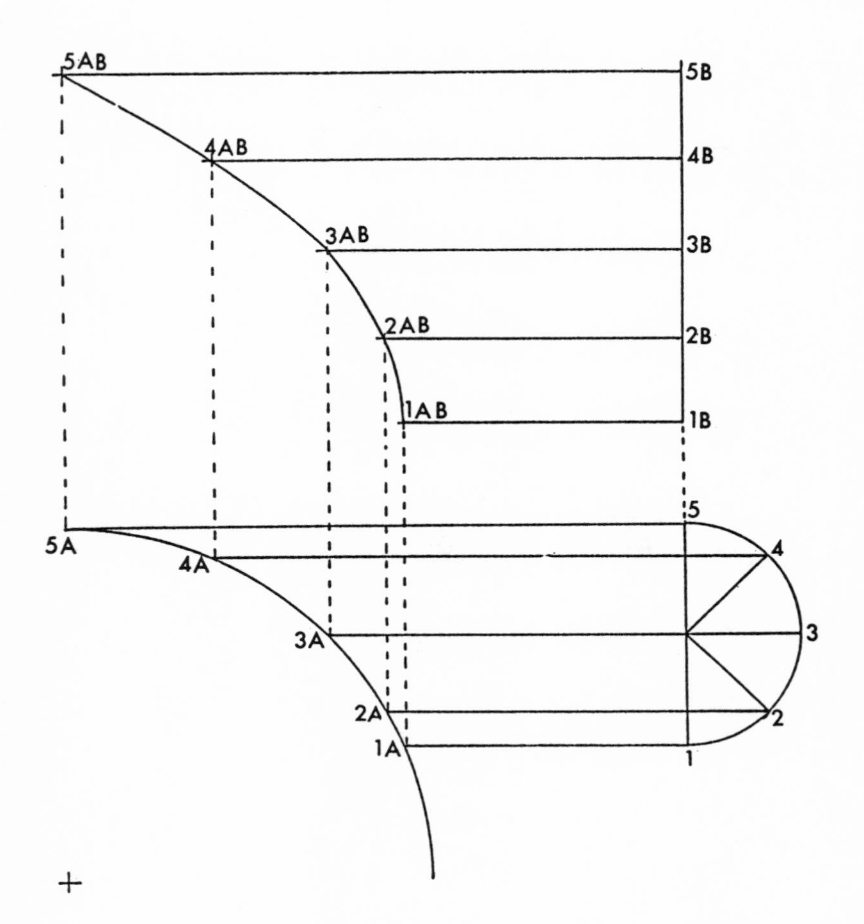

FIGURE 15

EXTEND VERTICAL PARALLEL LINES

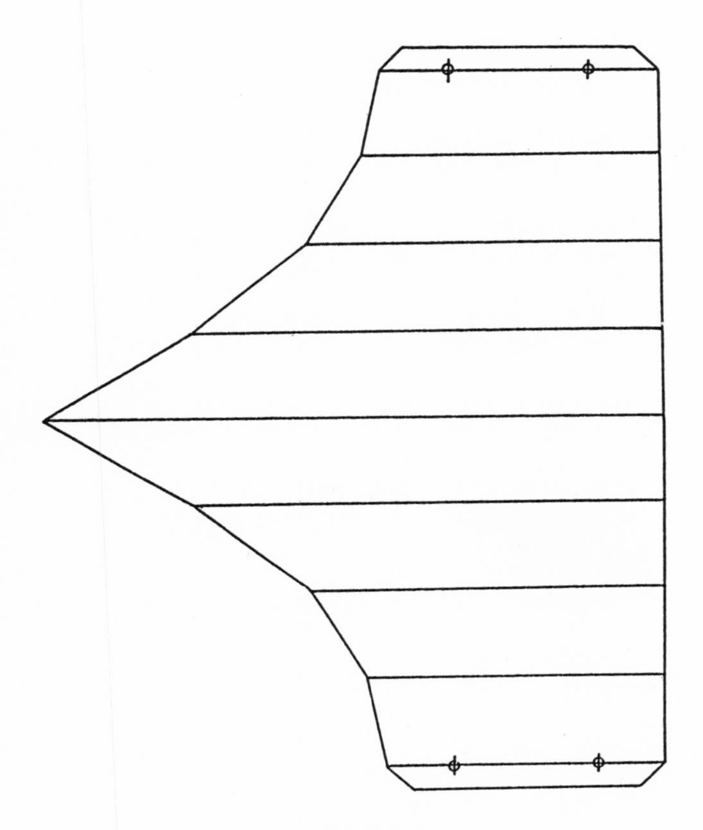

FIGURE 16

THE FULL LAYOUT

With all of the forms complete we can begin to build the furnace body.

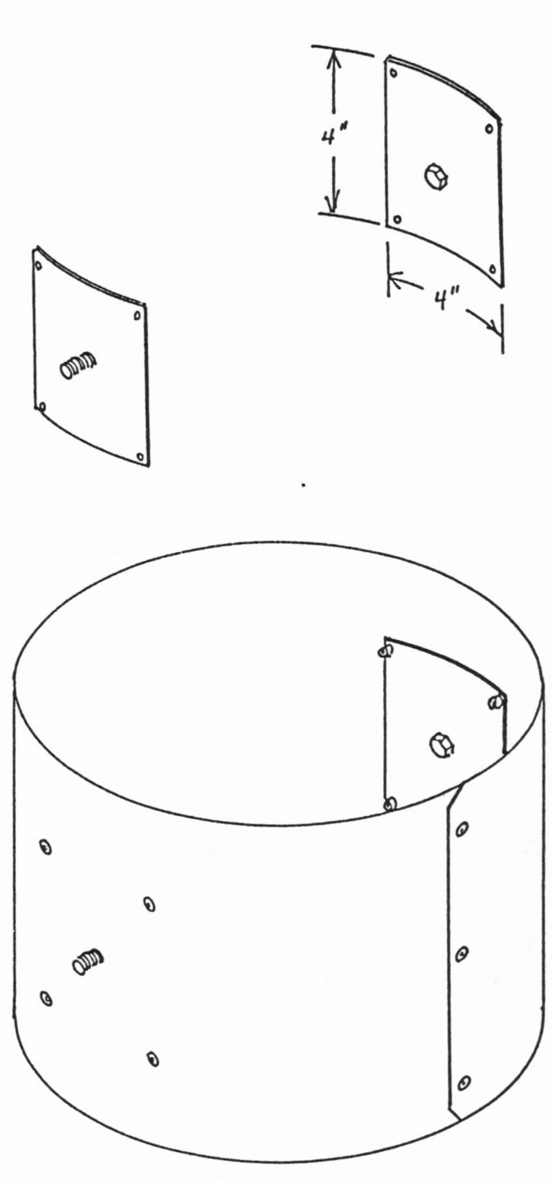

FIGURE 17

BUILDING THE CENTRAL BODY

A pair of reinforcement plates of heavy gauge metal, about 16 gauge and 4" square are prepared as in figure 17 with a 5/16" X 1/2" long bolt brazed or welded in a hole drilled through the center. They are curved to match the Central body form and fastened to the inside of the form with rivets or machine screws and nuts. These are the lifting studs that will fasten the central body to the lifting arms.

Cut a truly circular hole slightly larger than 13" in diameter in a piece of masonite, plywood or heavy corrugated cardboard to provide a close fit over the central body form. Three of these circular guides will be required. They are used to keep the forms truly circular and uniform so that they will fit nicely together when stacked later.

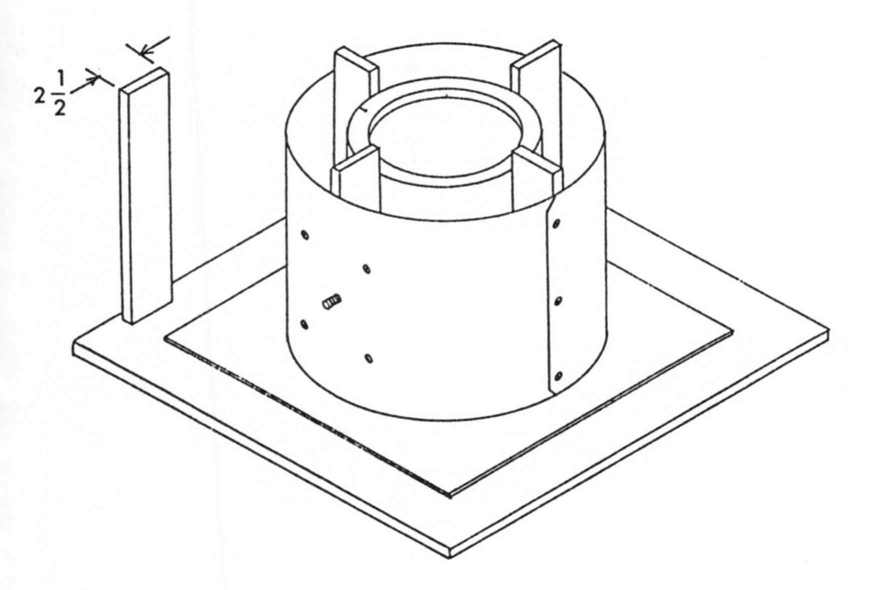

FIGURE 18

Cut four wooden spacers from scrap that will be used to hold the inside form concentric with the outside form.

Assemble all of these components over a piece of plywood about two feet square as shown in figure 18. If you are using the home blend refractory this should be a rough grade of plywood since it will be sacrificed when you fire the lining. In that case it must also have a hole of about 3" diameter in the middle to provide combustion air for the fire.

Now it is a simple matter to fill the form with prepared refractory mix as you gradually withdraw the wooden spacers. Tamp the mix in with a stick of wood and be sure to leave no voids. If you are using a commercial castable mix it will be somewhat wetter than the home blended mix and you can rap the form to release trapped air. If you are using the home blend mix it will be stiffer and your tamping should be more in the nature of ramming so that it will be very densly packed, but don't distort the form. Fill the forms above the top and then stike off level with a straight edge.

If you are using the commercial castable refractory simply allow the filled form to set over night before you remove the inside form. Be sure and follow any special directions that are furnished with the refractory mix. Remove the collapsible inside form only after the lining has firmly set up.

If you are using the home blend refractory you can fire the lining immediately provided that it is not too wet. Otherwise you must wait until it is stiff enough to remove the inside form. If it is neccessary to dry the lining you must do it gradually. Cover it with a damp cloth and keep the cloth damp at all times. It may take two or three days to cure. The water in the mix will evaporate gradually but the skin must not be allowed to dry out. When it is stiff enough remove the inside form and fill any voids that might be there. But handle the lining gently for now. It will have no strength until it is fired. If you do not fire immediately keep it covered with a damp cloth until you do.

FIRING THE CENTRAL BODY LINING

If you are using the commercial castable refractory there is no need to fire the lining until the furnace is assembled. But the home brewed lining must be fired to vitrify it. It is easy to do with a charcoal fire.

Carefully move the filled form outside some distance from any buildings and set it upon three or four bricks so that air can enter the hole in the base board. Put a double layer of charcoal briquettes inside the form and soak them with starting fluid. If the lining is stiff enough to remove the form it will not be harmed by the charcoal if you are reasonably gentle. Ignite the charcoal and when it is well lit add more. Continue to add charcoal as the fire grows until the entire form is filled with burning coals. Eventually the wooden base will ignite and the fire will fall through so just add more charcoal and keep the fire going for at least two hours. At first steam will be seen escaping and it will gradually lessen. You want the inside of the lining to become bright red hot to thoroughly vitrify the clay. The wood will burn away entirely and when the fire begins to die you can cover the top with a sheet of metal and allow it all to cool gradually for a few hours or over night.

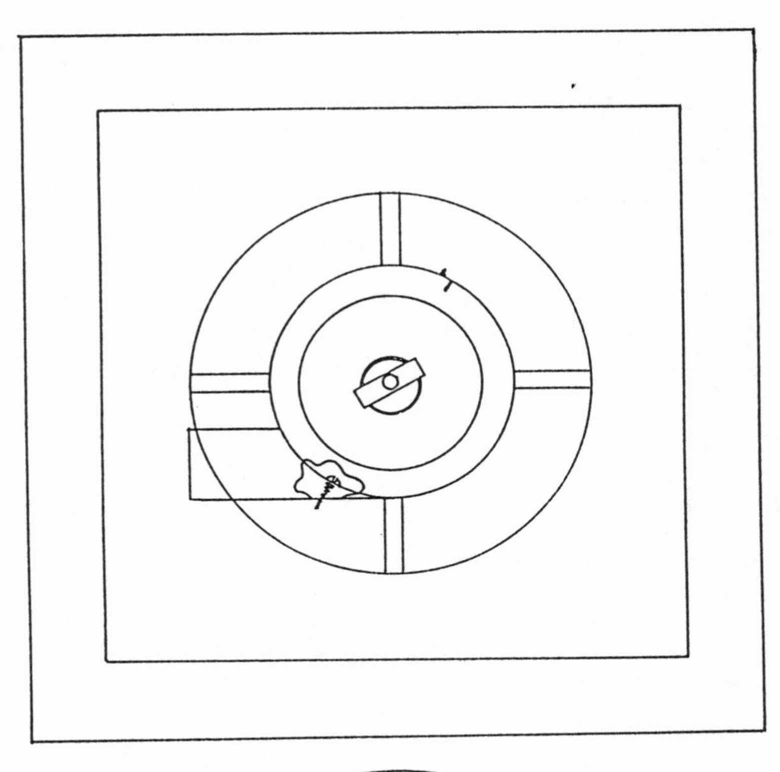

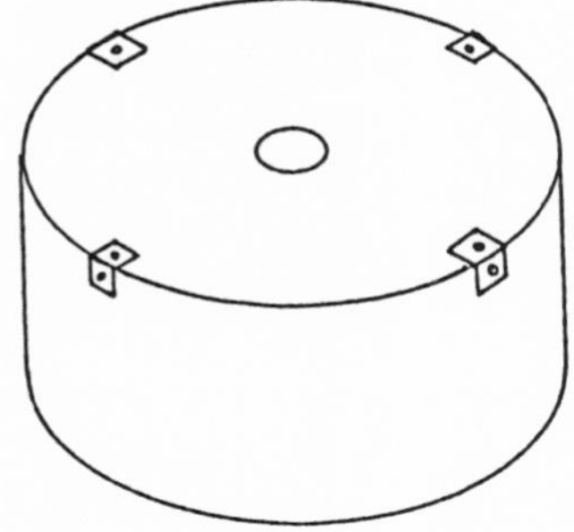

FIGURE 19

BUILDING THE BASE

Cut a disc of sheet metal 13" in diameter with a 2" diameter hole in the center and fasten it to the bottom of the base form with at least four sheet metal angles as in figure 19. Blind rivets will serve nicely for this job. The fit does not have to be close but you want a neat appearance. It will be best to use the plywood circular guide as you fasten the bottom in place.

With the circular guide resting on another piece of plywood fasten the 2" diameter form for the safety hole in position over the center hole in the base form with a scrap of strap iron and a long screw or lag bolt as shown in figure 19.

Fill the form with refractory mix to a depth of 2 1/2". If you are using the commercial castable refractory you may want to allow it to set up stiff before you continue. Then set the collapsible inside form in place and insert the burner inlet tube through the hole in the side of the base form. It is fastened to the inside form with a single sheet metal screw from the inside as shown in figure 19. It will be easiest to pre-drill the screw holes on the bench before you install the inside form. The wooden guides center the form. Fill the remaining area of the form with refractory, taking care to tamp it in well around the burner inlet form. Strike it off level with the top of the form and smooth the surface with a trowel.

If you are using the commercial castable refractory simply let it set over night before you remove the inside form. The burner inlet form is left in place when the temporary inside form is removed.

FIRING THE BASE LINING

Again the commercial refractory need not be fired but the home brewed lining must be fired.

Prepare a ring of scrap sheet metal a little larger than 13" in diameter and about 4" deep so that it can be used to extend the height of the form for the firing operation.

Carefully move the filled form outside on its base and set it on a level place away from buildings. Make sure that the lining is stiff enough before you remove the inside form. Don't forget to remove the screw that holds the burner inlet form before you loosen the inside form. Also carefully remove the safety hole form. Set the extension ring on the form so that the coals can be heaped over the top. Fasten it with a couple of sheet metal screws if neccessary. Combustion air will enter at the burner inlet so there is no need for a hole in the bottom.

Set a double layer of charcoal briquettes inside, soak them with starting fluid and ignite them. Continue to add charcoal as the fire grows until it is mounded full of burning coals. Add fuel as neccesary to keep the fire going strong for at least two hours. Then when the fire begins to die cover it with a scrap of sheet metal and let it cool gradually for a few hours.

BUILDING THE LID

The form for the lid is drilled with sixteen 1/8" holes in addition to the four holes that are used to join it at the seam. Notice that eight of these holes are drilled at 2" intervals while the remainder are at 2 3/4" intervals. This is done so that a neat square grid pattern can be woven in with wire.

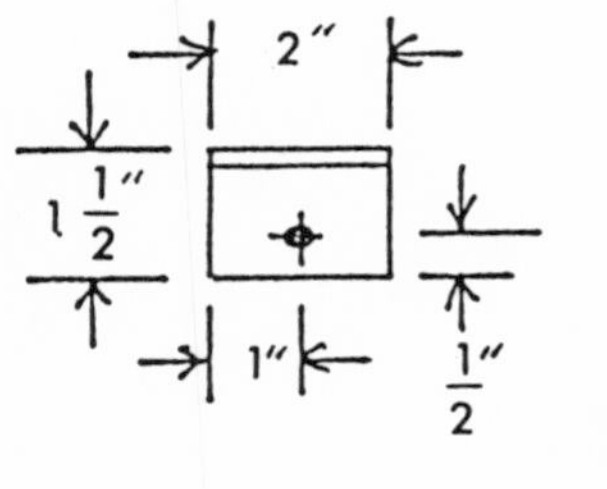

FIGURE 20
MAKE TWO

A pair of brackets are made from 1 1/2" X 1/8" angle iron as in figure 20. And a handle similar to that shown in figure 21 will be required. You can purchase a barn door handle or make one from 1/2" or 3/4" electrical conduit as shown in figure 21.

Set the lid form in the circular guide and weave the mesh of 16 gauge wire through the holes in the rim as shown in figure 22. When the pattern is complete simply bring the ends of the wire inside the rim and twist them around any portion of the grid. Do not attempt to make the grid tight as you weave it for you will distort the form. Just make it neat and symmetrical and then give each strand a little twist with pliers as shown in figure 23 to snug it up when finished.

Bolt the handle and the brackets to the form as shown in figure 22. The spacing of the brackets is to fit the outside diameter of the 1" pipe used for the lid standard.

Fasten the vent hole form in the center with a scrap of strap iron and a long screw or a lag bolt.

Fill the form with refractory mix, tamp it in solid and strike it off level with the form as shown in figure 24.

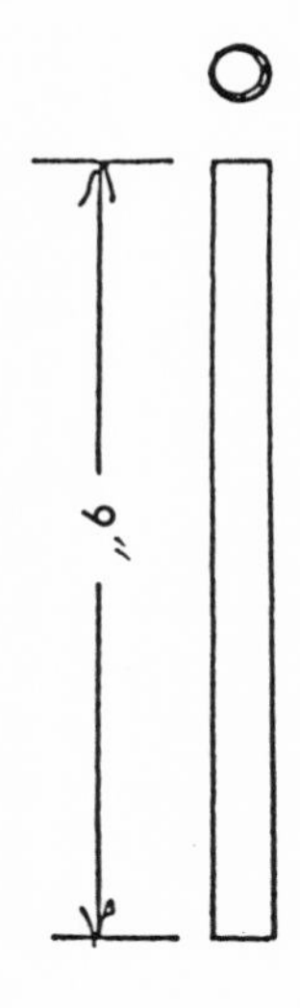

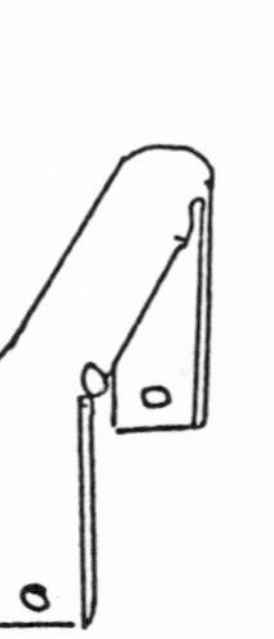

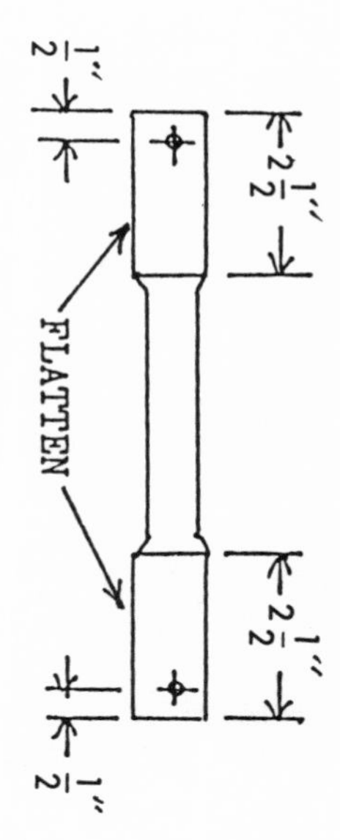

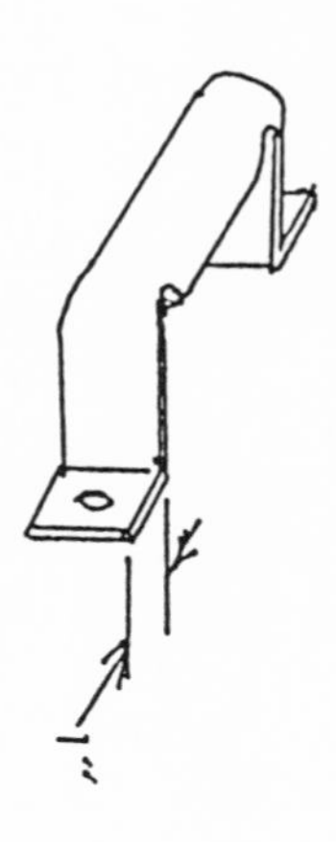

FIGURE 21 MAKE 1

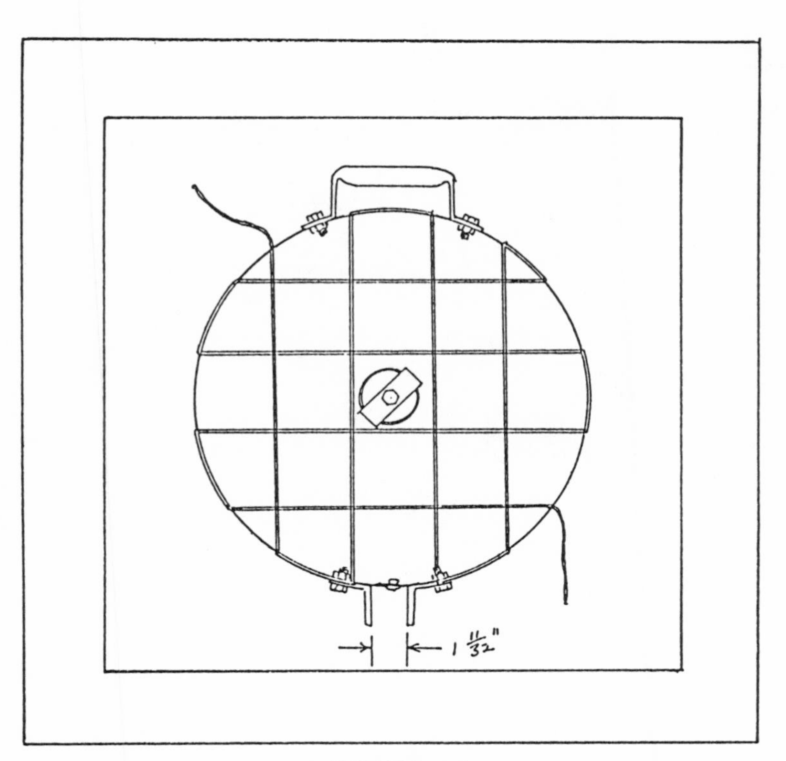

FIGURE 22

FIGURE 23

FIGURE 24

FIRING THE LID

You can use the same extension ring you used for the base to raise the coals above the surface of the lid. Some slots cut around the edge with tabs bent will allow for some combustion air. Again the fire is gradually built up until the extension ring is mounded full. Keep the fire going strong for a couple of hours but don't smother it this time. Rake the coals into a pan and set them aside as you place a piece of plywood on the lid and turn it over. Then slide the original base board off and set it aside. Set the extension ring in place and fire the second side of the lid for a couple more hours before smothering the fire. This procedure will ensure that the lid is thoroughly fired before you attempt to lift it.

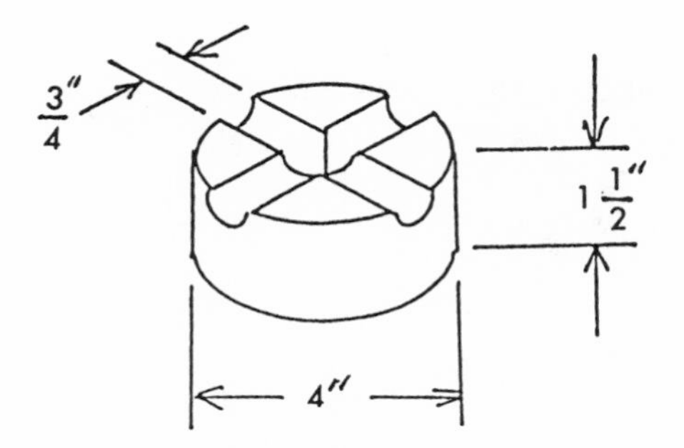

FIGURE 25

THE PLINTH

Any circular form such as a piece of mailing tube, cereal box or plastic container that is about 4" in diameter and 1 1/2" deep will do to mold the plinth. It will be a good idea to make two or three because they get severe use and must be replaced from time to time. Notice in figure 25 that there are grooves in the bottom of the plinth. These can be formed with a 3/4" dowel or an old broom stick, or simply cut them with a trowel.You might fire the plinth by setting it on the lid or you can wait and fire it in the furnace when it is complete.

GLAZING THE LINING

Authorities differ in opinion whether the lining of the furnace should be glazed. The commercial castable refractories will certainly be durable without glazing but you may want to add a glaze to the home-brewed lining. There are many ceramic glazes available from dealers in ceramics supplies that are used to glaze the refractory linings of kilns. They are called 'kiln wash'. They are applied in liquid form and the kiln is heated to fuse them to the lining. The proprietary blends are very good but if you can't find them you can make your own. The essential ingredients are ground glass, clay and borax.

Begin by pulverizing two or three beverage bottles. Some claim that green bottles are best, such as a famous soft drink that came in green bottles for decades. I like brown beer bottles myself. What is important is to reduce them to sand again. BE CERTAIN TO WEAR EYE PROTECTION WHEN YOU PULVERIZE BOTTLES! I put the bottles in a sack and break them into small pieces first. Then I stand a 16" length of 1 1/4" pipe on a cake of iron or steel about 1/2" thick and drop a few pieces of glass into the pipe. I pound the glass with a length of 3/4" steel rod about two feet long to pulverize it. This improvised mortar and pestle greatly reduces the danger, but occasional chips of glass fly about so you must be careful for yourself and any bystanders. I sift the stuff through a small tea strainer and return all that won't pass to the mortar for another pounding. It does not take so very long to get up a good amount of powdered glass.

Add to the ground glass one half its volume of fire clay and one fourth its volume of borax powder. Mix the dry ingredients very thoroughly. Then add water and mix to the consistency of thinned paint. (Like rich cream) Mix only enough for each use.

To apply the glaze first wet the furnace lining by brushing on water. Then apply a uniform coat of glaze with a brush. You must stir it often and add water from time to time for it tends to settle and thicken as you work. It will be best to use a cardboard gasget between each joint in the furnace to prevent the glaze from fusing the sections together.

Run the furnace up to a bright red or orange heat and the glaze will fuse to the lining to leave a hard and durable surface.

PATCHING THE LINING

The same blend of ingredients as used for the home brewed lining can be used for repairs when they become neccessary. You can allow the remnant of the original batch to dry out and add water when you use it. Or you can store it in an air tight container to be ready to use at any time.

The patching material will fire to the same quality as the original lining but it will not adhere unless you prepare the surface properly. First clean off the surface of any loose material and blow out any dust in the damaged area. Then mix up a slurry of fire clay and water and brush it on the damaged area like paint. Immediately trowel in the repair material. You can fire it immediately.

Of course very thin patches will not hold well but areas of 1/2" thickness will generally hold quite well. The home-brewed lining will certainly not be as durable as the commercial castable products and it will have to be replaced entirely from time to time.

CHAPTER III
BUILDING THE FURNACE FRAME

The furnace frame is a simple weldment of common angle iron and strap iron. Figure 26 shows a top plan view and side elevation with essential dimensions. The lower portion provides a platform for the furnace base and the vertical portion provides the track for the body raising mechanism. Notice that the lower portion is of 1 1/4" angle iron while the vertical track is 1 1/2" angle iron. Figure 27 shows an angular view of the completed frame with the lid lifting mechanism added.

MATERIALS REQUIRED

4' 1 1/2" X 1/8" angle iron
6' 1 1/4" X 1/8" angle iron
17' 1" X 1/8" angle iron
4' 1" X 1/8" strap iron
3' 1/2" X 1/8" strap iron
4' 1/2" black pipe
24 1/2" 1" black pipe
14" 1 1/4" black pipe
18" 1/4" diameter rod or all thread

In addition to the above listed structural iron materials you will need four sliding glass patio door rollers. These are available in hardware and building supplies as repair parts. Described as "Universal design, 1 1/2" diameter, steel ball bearing rollers with steel inner race and 1/4" hole".

The pivots in the mechanisms are made with 1/4" soft iron rivets, which can be found in hardware departments. You can also cut short lengths of 1/4" mild steel rod or the shanks of 1/4" bolts to make the rivets. A one pound hammer will cold set such small rivets. The remainder of the fastening will be done with small machine screws and nuts.

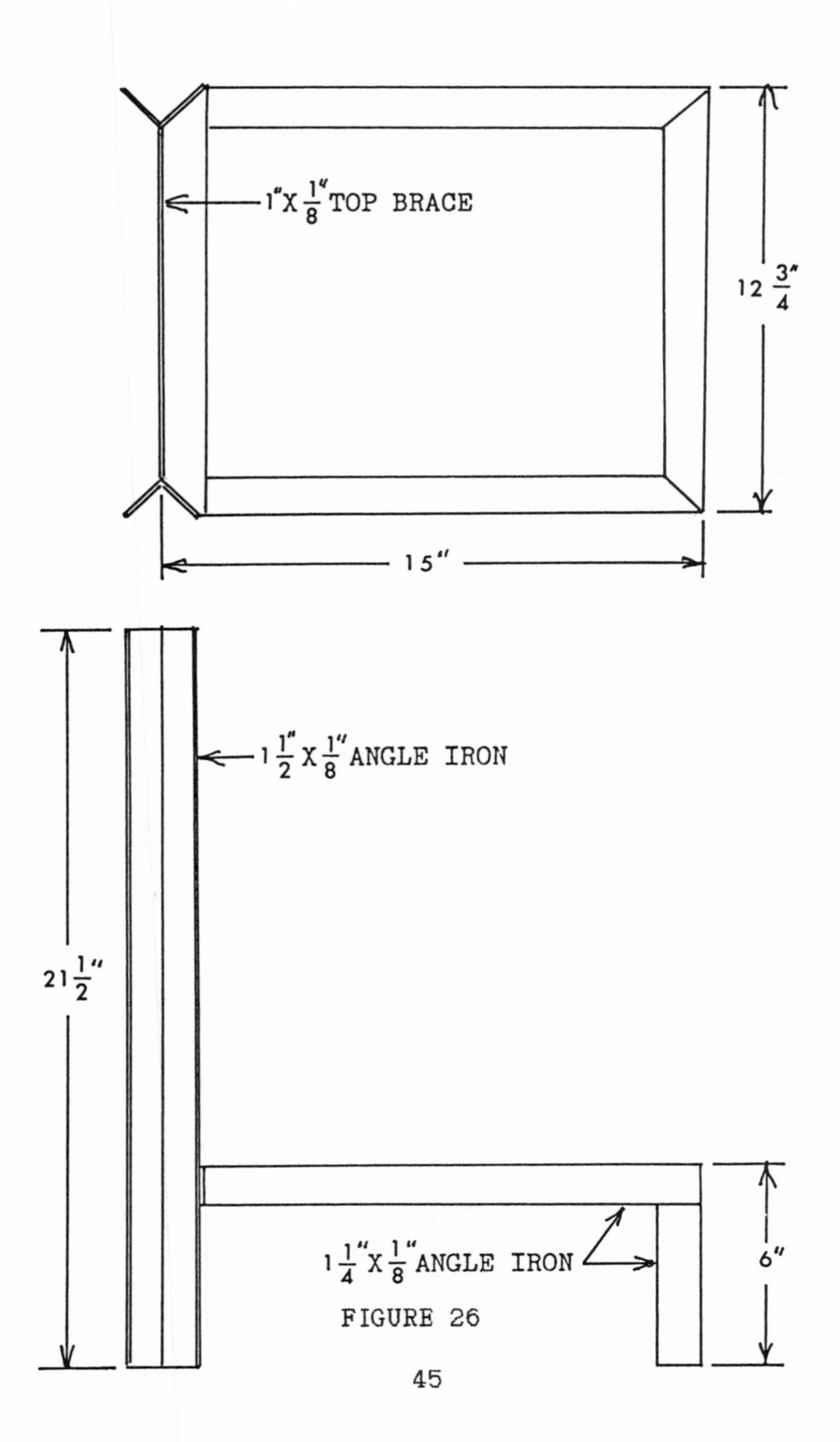
1"X 1/8" TOP BRACE
12 3/4"
15"
21 1/2"
1 1/2" X 1/8" ANGLE IRON
1 1/4" X 1/8" ANGLE IRON
6"
FIGURE 26

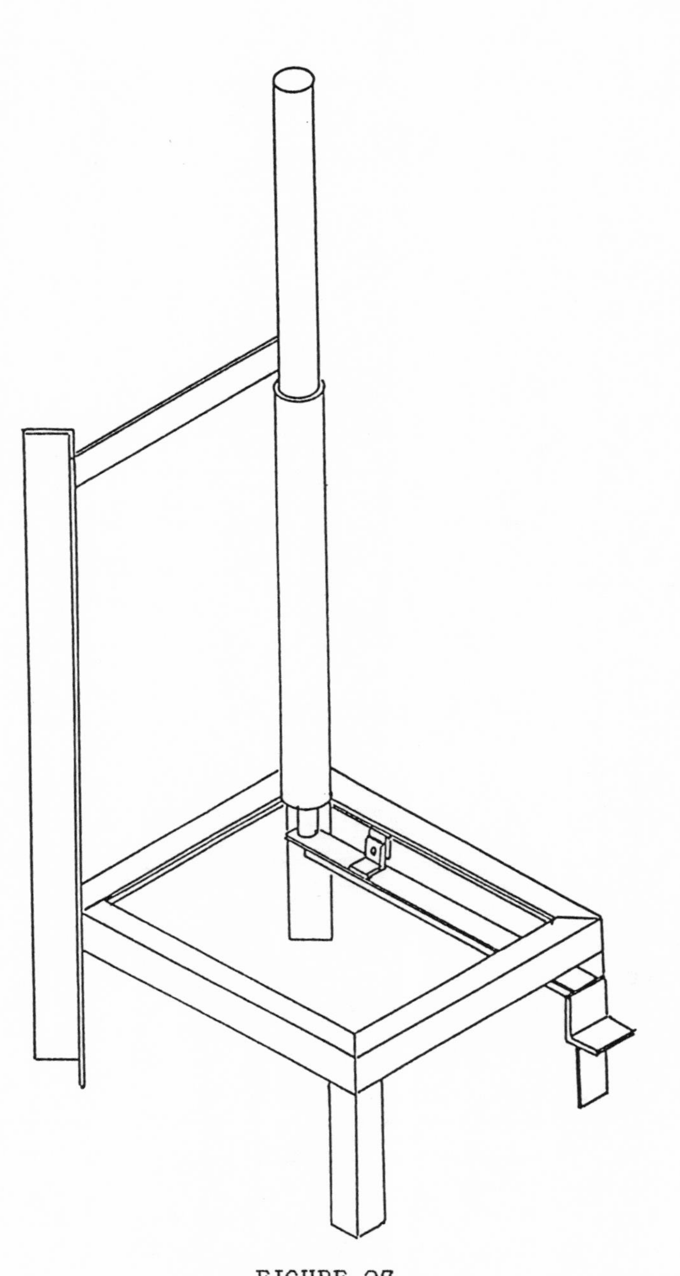

FIGURE 27

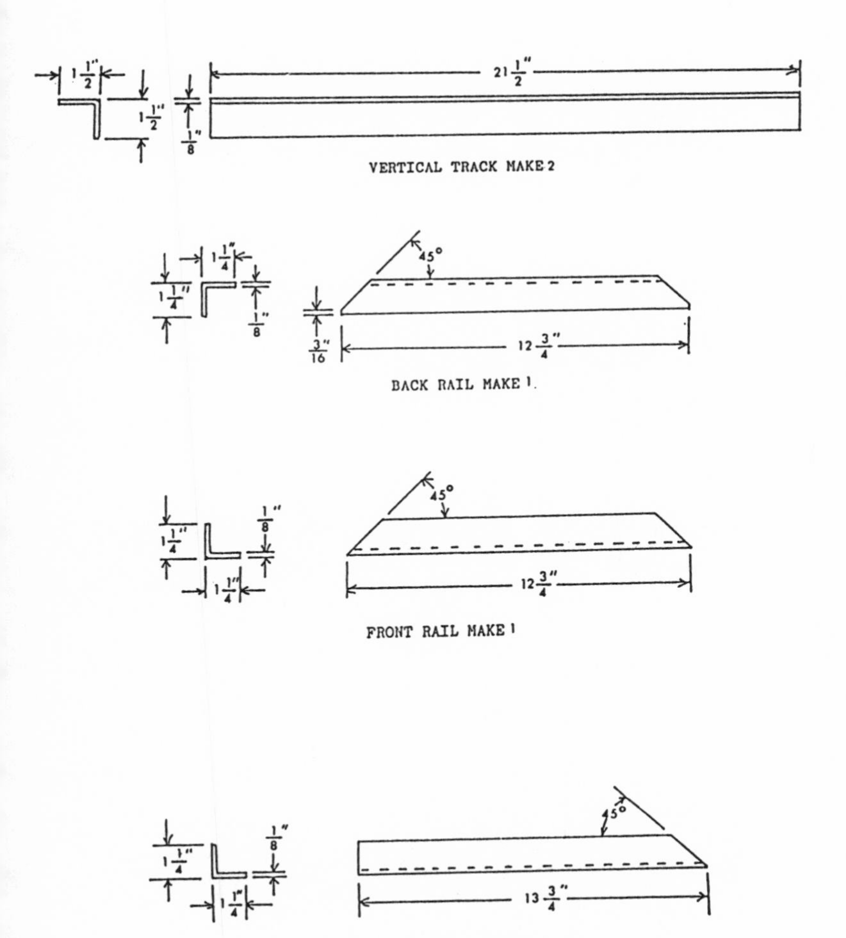

FIGURE 28

ASSEMBLE THE FRAME

Cut the pieces of angle iron as shown in figure 28. In addition to these cut two 4 3/4" lengths of 1 1/4" X 1/8" angle iron for the front legs and a 10 1/2" length of 1" X 1/8" strap iron for the top brace. Don't forget that the vertical track is 1 1/2" angle while the remainder of the frame is of 1 1/4" angle.

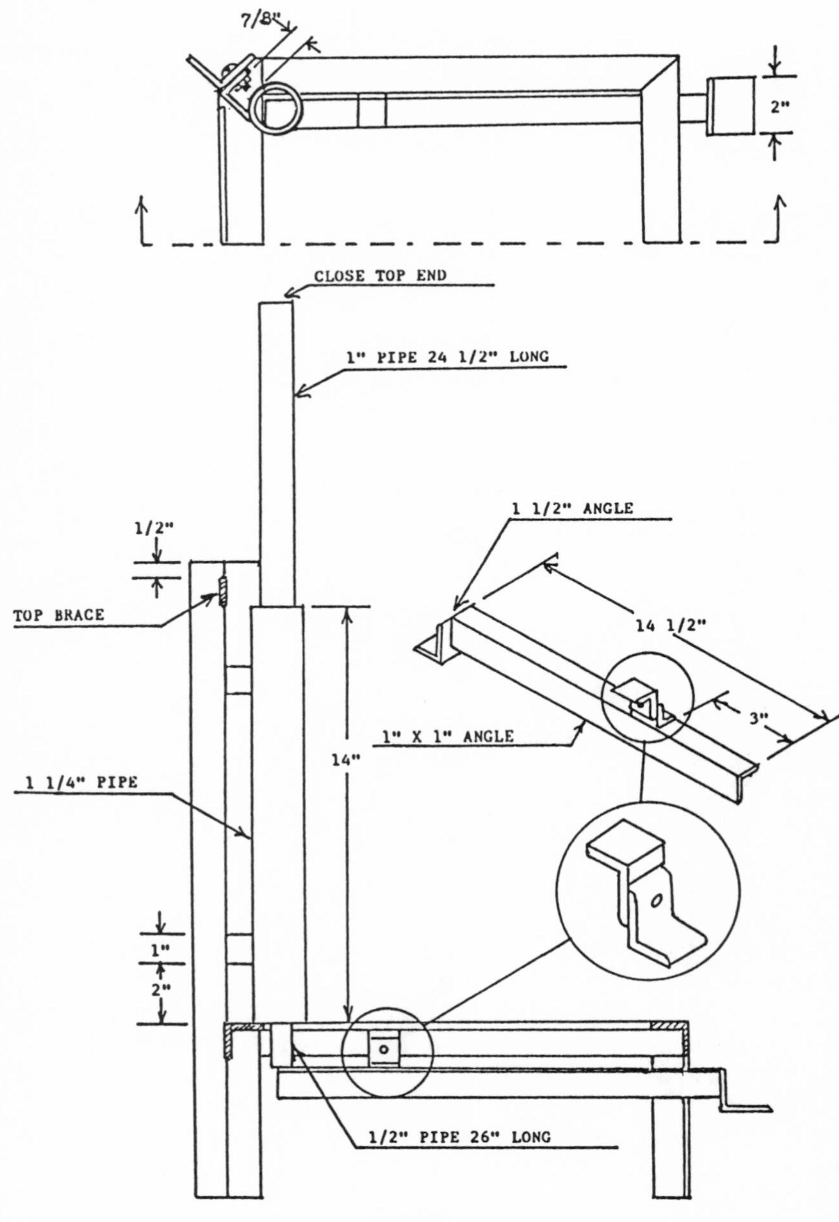
7/8"
2"
CLOSE TOP END
1" PIPE 24 1/2" LONG
1 1/2" ANGLE
1/2"
TOP BRACE
14 1/2"
3"
1" X 1" ANGLE
14"
1 1/4" PIPE
1"
2"
1/2" PIPE 26" LONG

FIGURE 29

Fit the parts together and tack weld them from the underside. Note that the front and back corners are fit differently to facilitate positioning the vertical tracks. When the lower frame is nicely squared up weld it up securely. Tack weld the front legs in place and then clamp the vertical tracks in place and tack weld them. Take special care to position the tracks truly vertical both front to back and side to side, and also parallel to each other. It will be best to tack weld the top brace in place before you permanently weld the tracks to the rails. The position of the top brace is shown in figure 29. There will be a rather wide gap where the side rail joins the vertical track and there you can weld a bit of scrap on the inside to close the gap and make a strong joint.

THE LID RAISING MECHANISM

All of the details for the lid raising mechanism are shown in figure 29. It will be best to begin with the guide tube, which is a 14" length of 1 1/4" black iron pipe.

The mounting brackets are made from 1" lengths of 1 1/2" angle iron by cutting 1/2" off of one leg on each bracket so that it will not interfere with the roller on the vertical track. There is 7/8" space between the bracket and the guide tube as shown in the upper detail in figure 29. A strip of scrap wood can be used as a spacer when you clamp the brackets to the pipe to weld them in place. Position the brackets 2" from each end of the guide tube as shown in the lower detail in figure 29.

Locate the guide tube so that it rests over the inside corner of the frame as shown in the upper detail in figure 29 and clamp the brackets to the vertical track. Drill one 3/16" hole through the track and each bracket and install one 3/16" machine screw with nut and lock washer in each bracket.

The lifting lever is a 14 1/2" length of 1" X 1/8" angle iron with a 2" length of 1 1/2" X 1/8" angle iron welded to one end for the foot pedal. The pivot is made from two 1" long scraps of 1" X 1/8" angle iron that are drilled 1/4" and joined with a 1/4" hammer set rivet. One leg of the pivot is welded to the lever 3" from the end opposite the foot pedal. The other leg of the pivot is welded to the side rail to position the end of the lever under the guide tube as shown in the upper detail of figure 29.

The lift rod is a 26" length of 1/2" black iron pipe. Just drop it into the guide tube to rest on the lever.

Weld a heavy washer or other metal disc in the end of the 24 1/2" length of 1" black iron pipe to form the lid standard. Slide the lid standard over the lift rod and into the guide tube to rest on the frame.

When the foot pedal is depressed the lid standard will raise. The lid brackets and struts will be welded to the lid standard at final assembly.

THE CENTRAL BODY LIFTING MECHANISM

This mechanism consists of a pair of lifting arms that ride the vertical track on ball bearing rollers. They are raised through a pair of offset links by a pair of levers that are joined by a length of 1/2" pipe which forms the lifting handle. At the top of the stroke the levers carry the link pivots over center and the mechanism is held in position by the weight of the central body section so that no latching device is required. The lever provides a two to one mechanical advantage to reduce the effort required to raise the body and lid. The lid lifting mechanism telescopes so that the lid raises with the central body. The few parts are easy to fabricate and assemble.

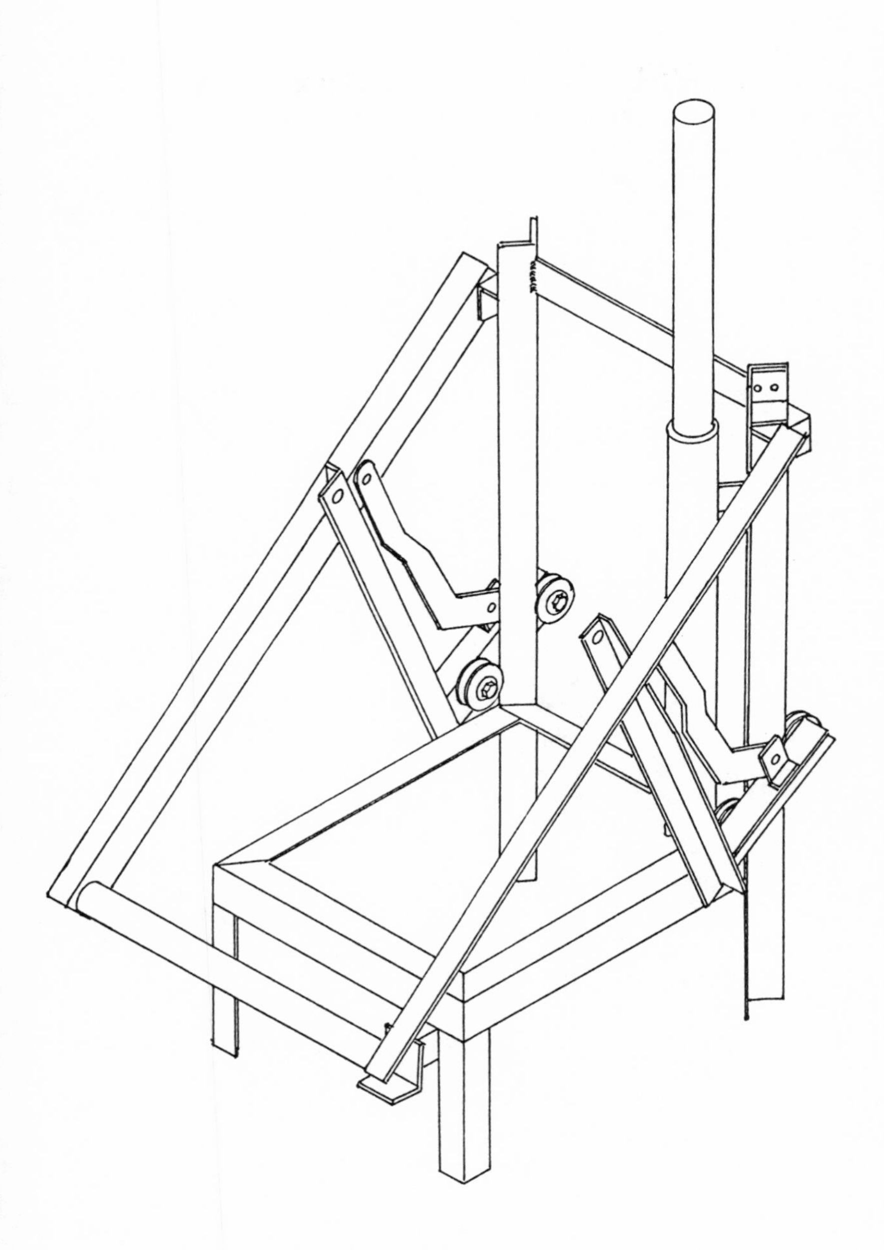

FIGURE 30

Figure 30 shows an angular view of the entire mechanism without the furnace sections in place. Figure 31 shows some views of the mechanism from inside, top and ends, as well as an angular view of the lifting arm pivot bracket.

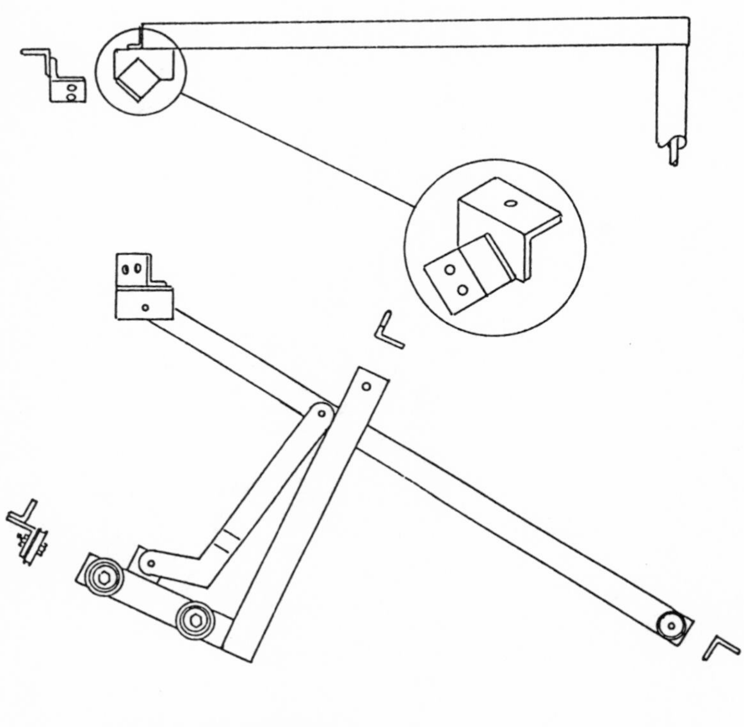

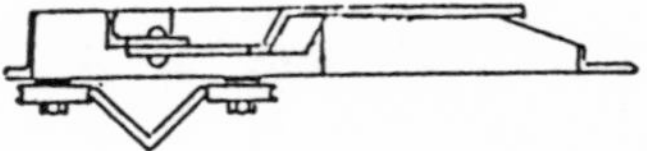

FIGURE 31

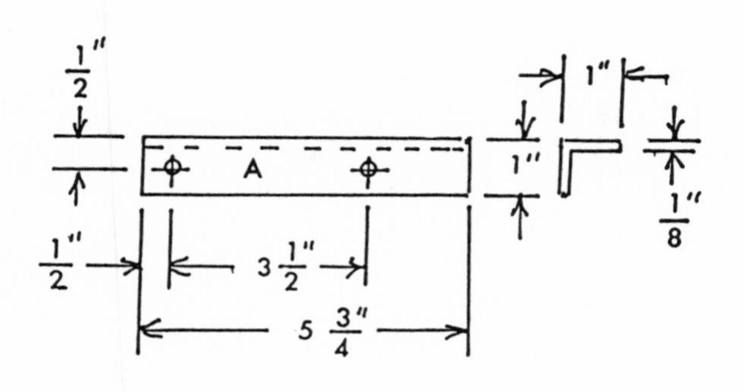

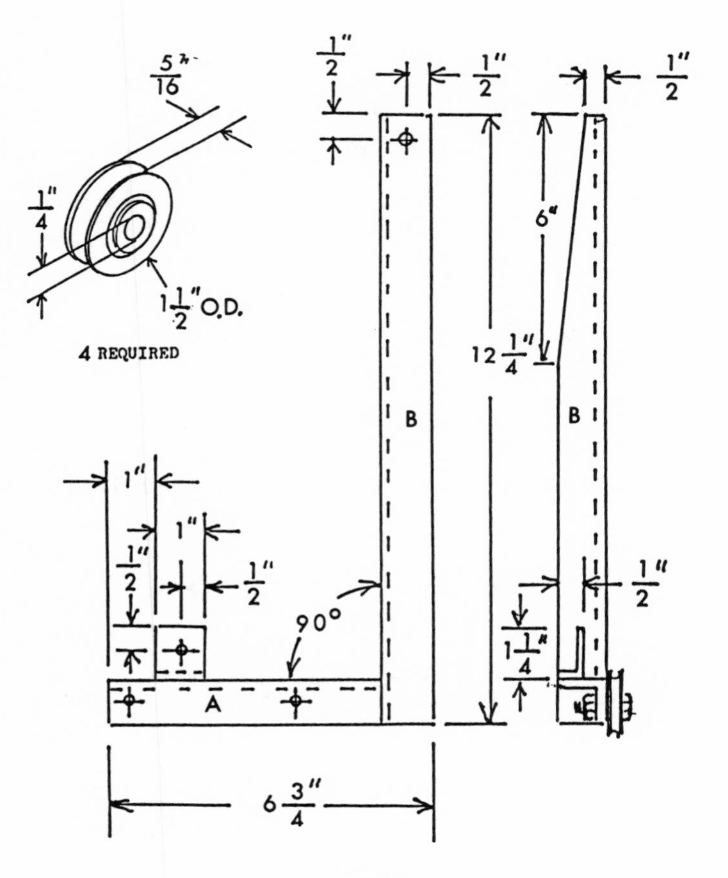

FIGURE 32
MAKE AN OPPOSING PAIR

THE LIFTING ARMS

An opposing pair is welded up of 1" X 1/8" angle iron. The details and dimensions are shown in figure 32. Locate the hole centers carefully and punch them before drilling. Notice that the upper portion of the arms is cut away at an angle to provide clearance for the link pivots. The cutting can be done with a hacksaw. It is not so vital that the members be joined at exactly 90 degrees as it is that they be as near identical as possible. You might weld up one of them to as near 90 degrees as possible and use it as a jig to weld the other one identically with holes aligned. The small link bracket is made from a scrap of 1 1/4" angle iron with one leg cut off to 1/2". It is drilled 1/4" for the link pivot. Mount two rollers on each arm with 1/4" bolts, nuts and lock washers.

THE LIFTING LEVERS

An opposing pair of levers are cut from 1" X 1/8" angle iron and drilled as in figure 33. A 15 1/4" length of 1/2" pipe is fastened between the lower ends with a length of 1/4" threaded rod with nuts and lock washers at both ends to form the lifting handle. Wooden bushings in each end of the pipe will center the threaded rod and make the handle firm and secure.

THE LIFTING LEVER PIVOTS

An opposing pair is made of 1 1/4" X 1/8" angle iron. Each pivot is made of two pieces of angle iron. The upper angle has two 3/16" mounting holes and the lower angle has a single 1/4" hole for the pivot pin. Clamp the upper angles at the top rear web of each vertical track and drill the 3/16" holes through both members as in figure 34. Install them with two 3/16" machine screws with nuts and lock washers. Clamp the lower angle to the upper angle and weld them together securely.

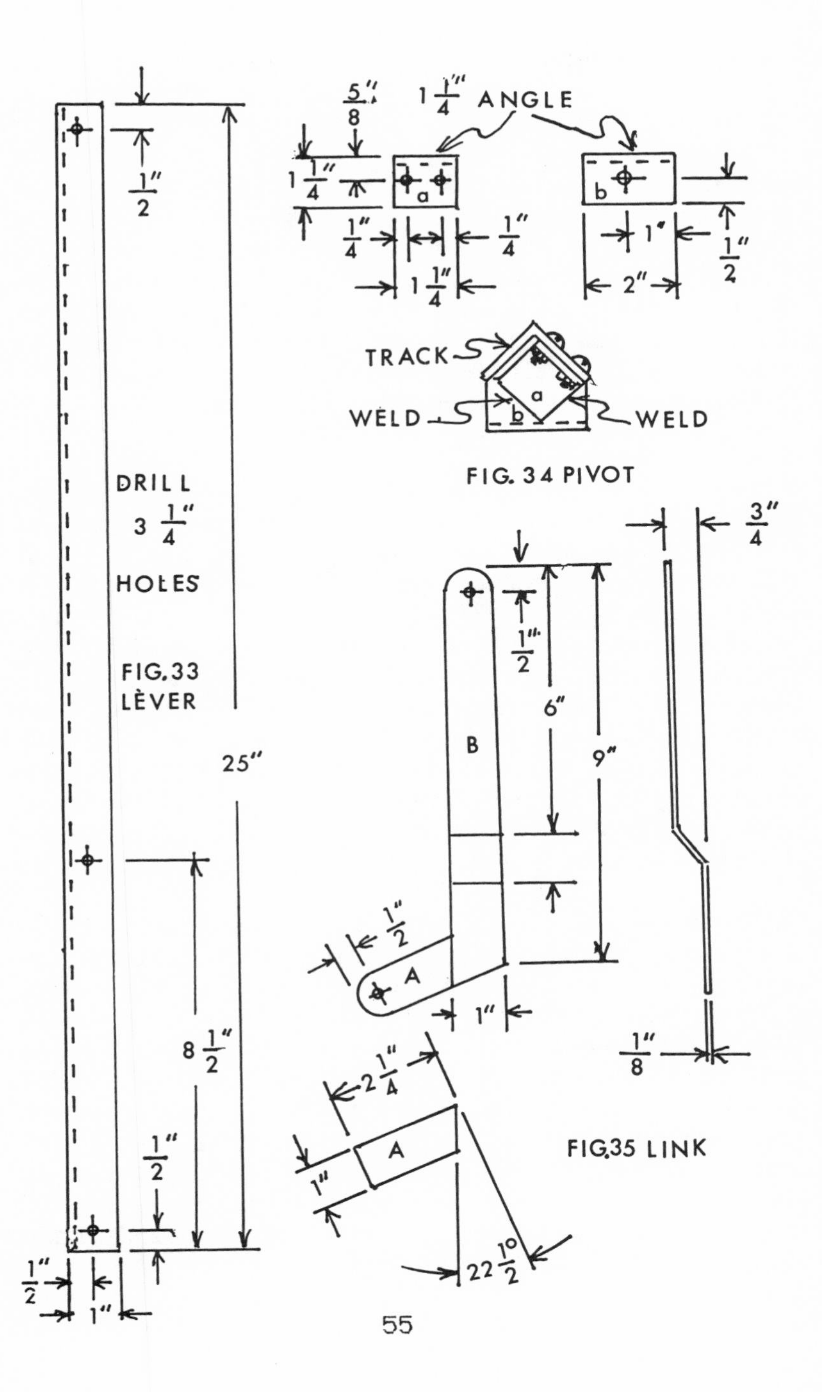

FIG. 33 LEVER

FIG. 34 PIVOT

FIG. 35 LINK

Remove the pivots from the tracks and rivet each to its respective lever with a 1/4" hammer set rivet.

THE OFFSET LINKS

Each is made of two pieces of 1" X 1/8" strap iron as dimensioned in figure 35. Note that the end of both members is cut to 22 1/2 degrees. Accuracy of the angle is not so critical but the links should be near identical. Weld them up securely and bend the offsets to make an opposing pair. Join the links to the lifting arms and lifting levers with 1/4" hammer set rivets as seen in figure 31.

FINAL ASSEMBLY

Make sure that all of the pivot joints are closely fit but they must work freely without binding. A drop or two of oil on each joint will help, and some hammer work will free them up if they bind. If the joints bind the furnace will tend to tip over backwards when you raise the lever but it will work nicely when the joints are free. Install the lever pivots and the lifting arms on the vertical track. The mechanism will not work well until the weight of the central body is on the lifting arms. This will be the best time to give the whole frame a coat or two of paint.

When the paint has dried set the base section on the frame with the burner inlet to the left as you face the unit. Set the central body on the base and fit the lifting arms over the studs. Install nuts, flat washers and lock washers on the studs and tighten them up. Raise the lifting handle several times so that the central body will park in its natural position. Oil the track a little and make sure the lifting mechanism is all working smoothly. Adjust the position of the base section as neccesary to align it with the central body section.

When all is well aligned and working smoothly you can fix the position of the base by bolting on four brackets made of scraps of 1" angle iron as shown in figure 36. It will be best to wait until the furnace has been fired a few times before you install these brackets.

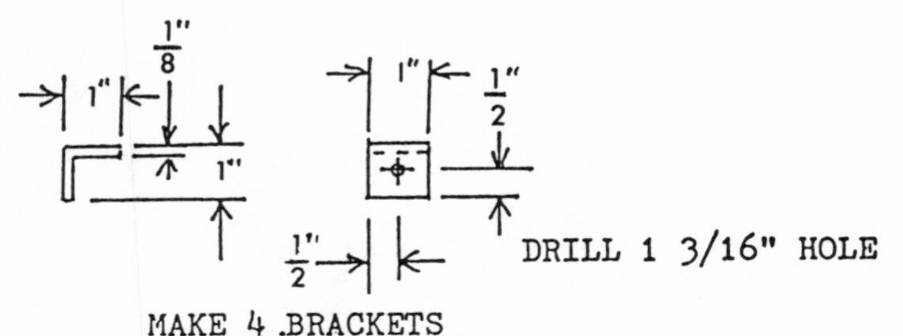

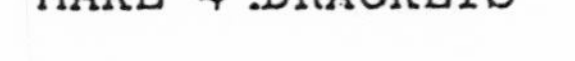

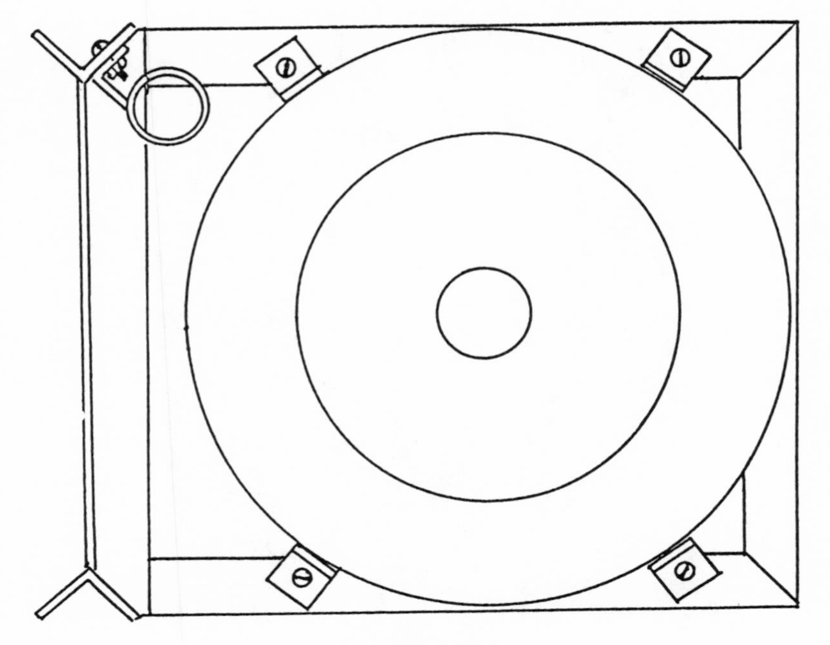

FIGURE 36

INSTALL THE LID

When the base and central body are well aligned and the lifting mechanism is working smoothly set the lid in place with its brackets on either side of the lid standard and tack weld the brackets to the standard. Two lengths of strap iron about 1/2" X 1/8" and 14 inches long will make suitable struts. Drill one end to fasten to the rim of the lid with a sheet metal screw and tack weld the other end to the top of the standard. When all is well aligned weld the brackets and studs securely.

The furnace is complete and ready for the burner. It will look like the photo in figure 37.

FIGURE 37

CHAPTER IV
BUILDING THE BURNER

The working principles of the burner have already been explained so we can set out to build without additional discussion. The elements of the burner include the stand, the motor/belt drive, the fan, the delivery tube and the electrical components. Since the fan involves the most detail it might be best to build it first.

This is an 8" centrifugal fan and both the wheel and the housing are built of sheet metal fastened together with screws and rivets. 26 gauge metal is adequate for all but the wheel, which should be 22 gauge or heavier. But you can make it of metal as heavy as you can manage to work. The outer curve of the housing is a 'volute', or an expanding spiral. The simple layout is done from three centers and it takes only minutes to do. The remainder of the shapes involved are easy circles and straight lines. While it is important to use a sharp scriber and do the layout as precisely as possible so that all of the parts fit together nicely, there is nothing technically demanding about building such a fan. Hole centers should be layed out carefully and punched before drilling. And mating parts should be drilled together for perfect alignment of holes.

A pair of wing dividers or a trammel will be needed for the circular layout. If you have neither you can improvise a trammel with a strip of light gauge sheet metal about 1" wide and 8" long. Simply scribe a line on the center of the strip and punch tiny holes with an awl at the center point and each radii as shown in figure 38. One awl is used to hold the center while another is used to scribe the arc. Simple and cheap! And you can throw it away and make another when the dimension requirements change.

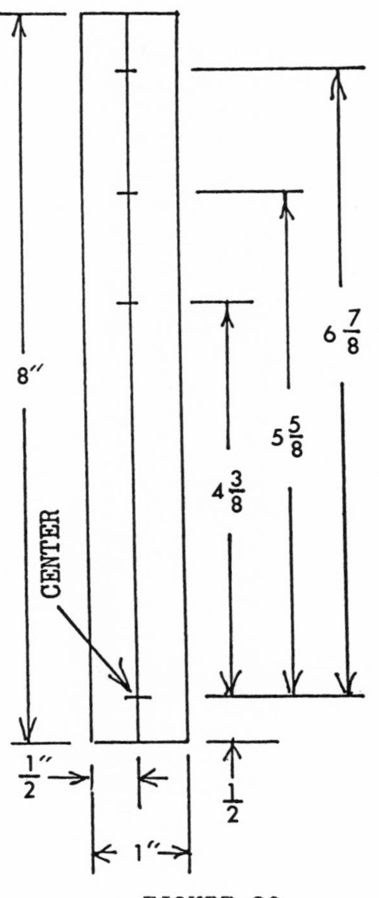

FIGURE 38

THE SCROLLS

These volute profiles form the front and back of the fan. The layout begins with a vertical line intersecting a horizontal line at right angles to establish the working center of the fan, marked "C" in figure 39. You can do the layout directly on a scrap of light gauge metal that can be used as a pattern. Mark centers "A" and "B" 5/8" on either side of center "C".

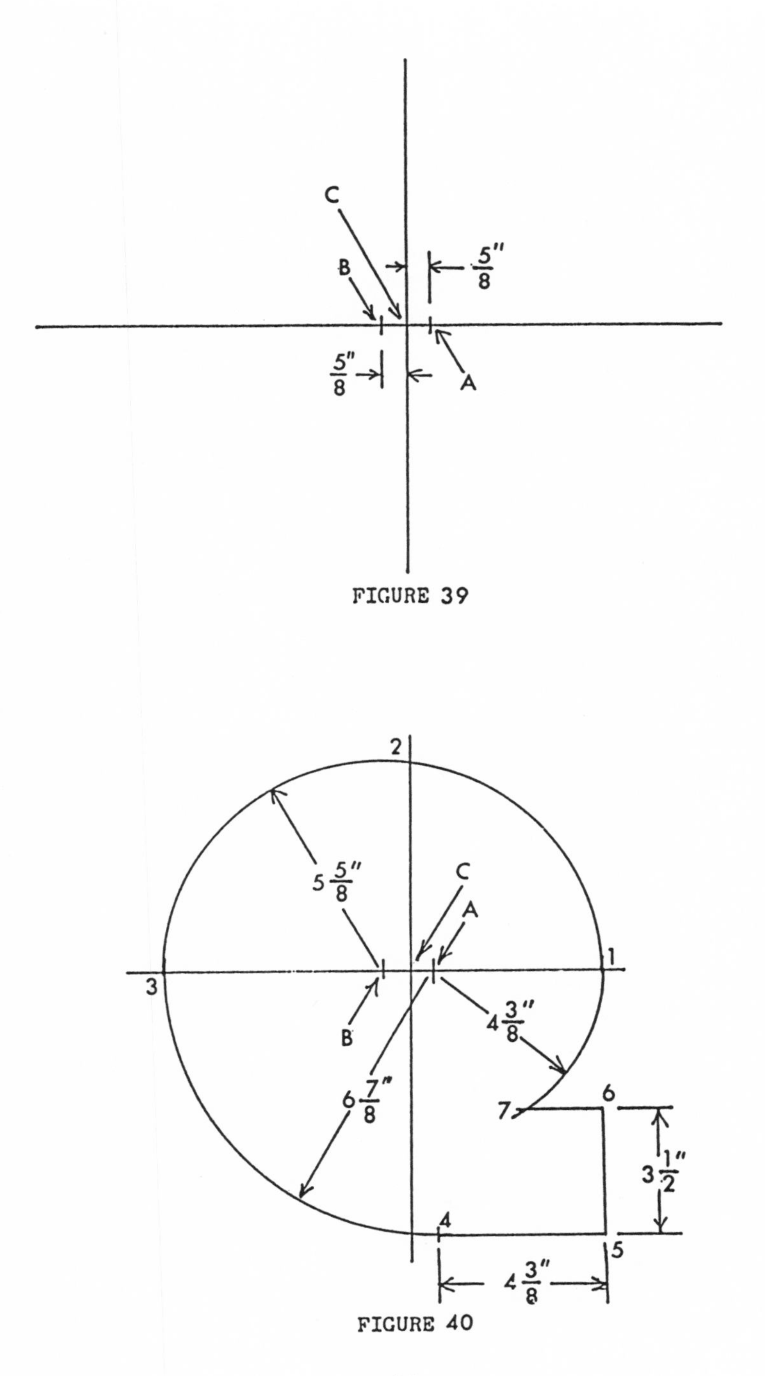

FIGURE 39

FIGURE 40

The entire layout appears in figure 40. Using center "A" and a 4 3/8" radius scribe an arc from the horizontal line at point 1 past point 7. (estimated) From center "B" with a radius of 5 5/8" scribe an arc from the horizontal line at point 1 to the opposite end of the horizontal line at point 3. From center "A" with a radius of 6 7/8" scribe an arc from the horizontal line at point 3, 5/8" past the vertical line to point 4. Notice that only centers "A" and "B" are used in the scroll layout. Center "C" is the working center of the fan. Now extend a horizontal line 4 3/8" from point 4 to point 5. Extend a vertical line 3 1/2" from point 5 to point 6. Finally extend a horizontal line from point 6 to intersect with the first arc at point 7 to complete the layout. This can be used for one of the scrolls if it is of heavy enough metal or you can use it for a pattern to make two identical. Don't forget to transfer the working center to each scroll by punching through the pattern.

The rear scroll has a hole just slightly larger than 5/8" diameter on the working center and the front scroll has a 3" diameter hole on the working center. Both scrolls are notched 3/8" square at the corners of the outlet as shown in figure 41. You can carefully scribe the 5/8" hole and enlarge it with a round file if you have no other tool to do the job. The 3" hole can be cut with aviation pattern snips, which you certainly must have to do much of the cutting out.

THE SHELL

The shell has a 3/8" flange bent up on both sides and it is rolled to shape on a simple plywood form that is 3/8" smaller in all its radii than the scrolls. Thus its final shape and dimension conforms to the scrolls and the members are assembled with sheet metal screws to form the housing.

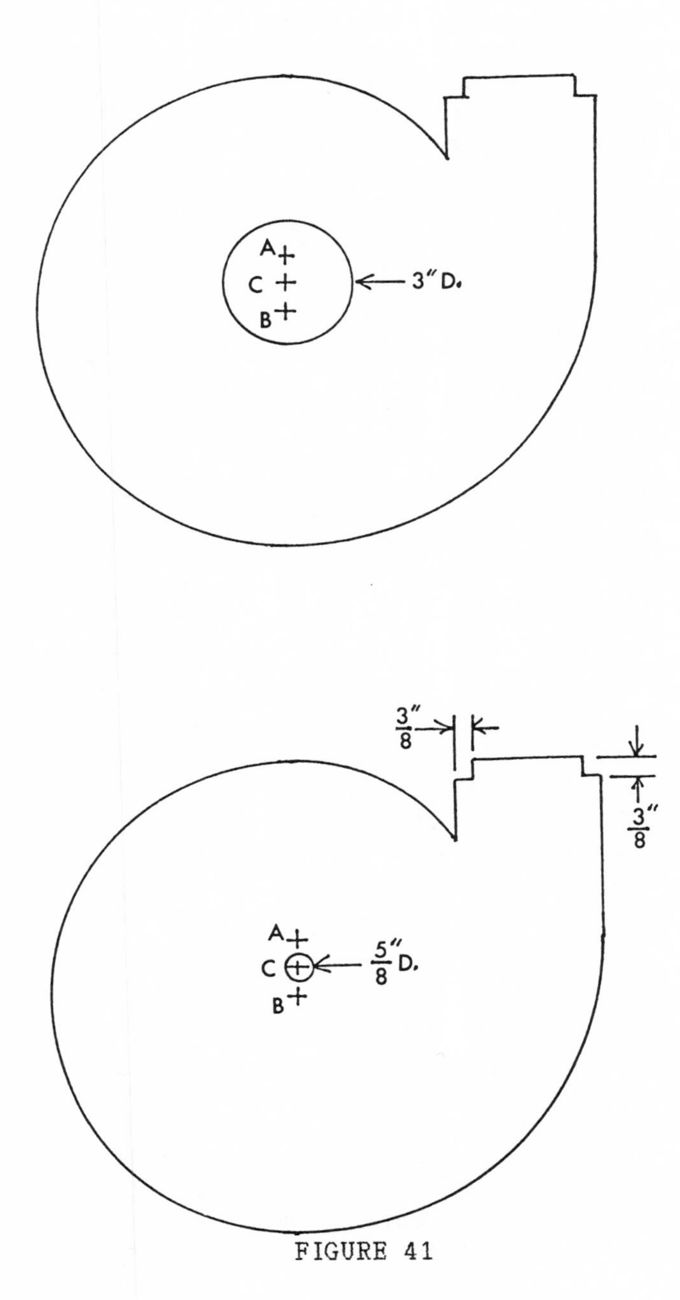

FIGURE 41

The layout of the plywood forms is exactly like that of the scrolls except for the dimensions. (Figure 42) 3/8" or 1/2" plywood of any grade is OK for the form. Cut out two identical and join them together with scraps of common wood to make a form 2" thick as shown in figure 44.

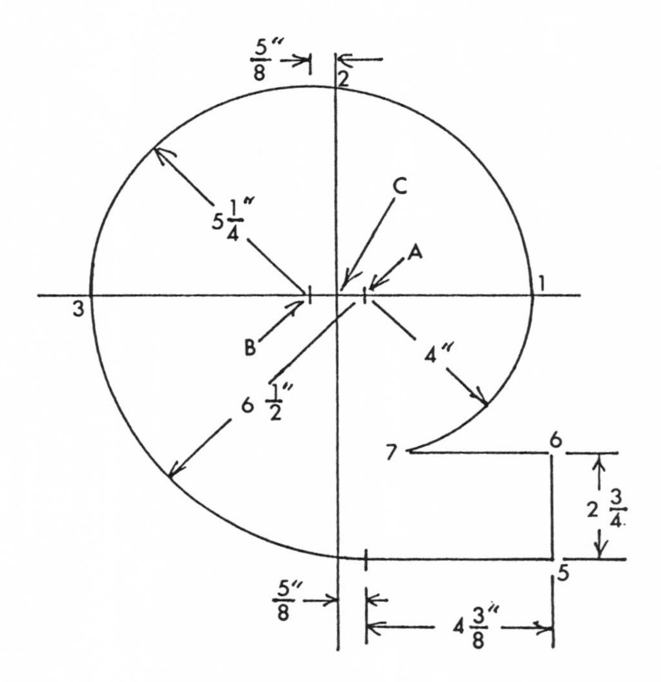

FIGURE 42

The shell itself is sheared to 39 1/4" by 2 3/4" and notched and bent as shown in figure 43. The 3/8" flange on each side reduces the width to 2". Make the return bend very sharp so that the shell can be fit into the form as in figure 45. Clamp it securely to the form and proceed to roll it around gradually. It will be neccessary to tap the flange on both sides with a hammer as you work to stretch it. Finally clamp the other end to the form.

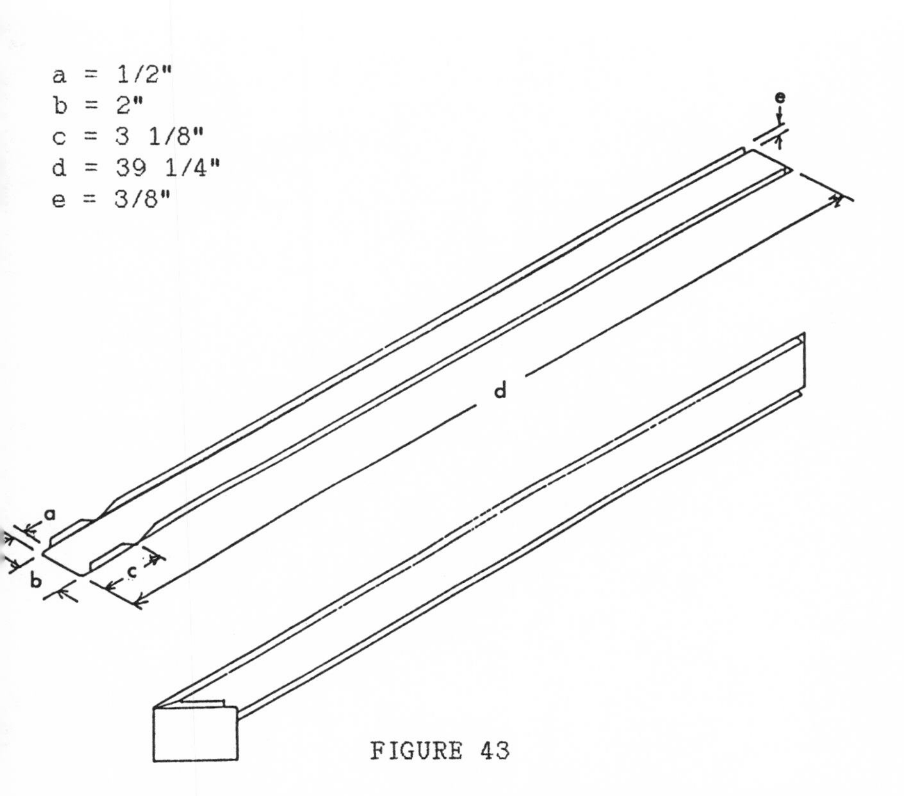

FIGURE 43

Be very careful of the sharp edges as you do this work. You can leave it clamped to the form as you install one of the scrolls with #8 X 1/2" self tapping sheet metal screws. Space the screws neatly at about 3" intervals. Some work with hammer and pliers will be neccessary to make a clean joint. It is not neccessary to have an air tight fit but of course you want a neat appearance. When one scroll is installed remove the form to install the second scroll as in figure 46.

When both scrolls are installed you can trim the ends of the shell and bend out four 3/8" flanges as in figure 47. The housing is complete except for the air shutter. The outside scroll will be removed to install the air shutter and to mount the fan housing on its angle iron stand.

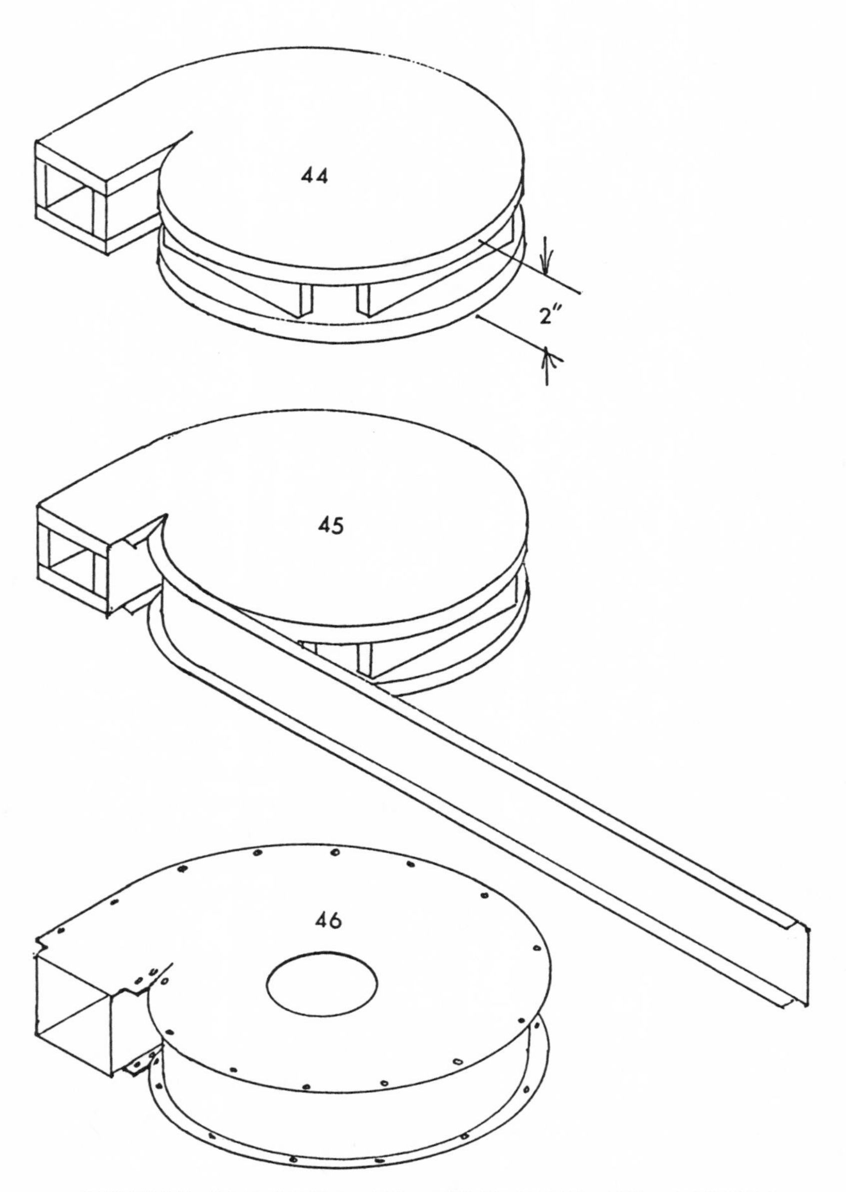

FORMING THE SHELL AND ASSEMBLING THE HOUSING

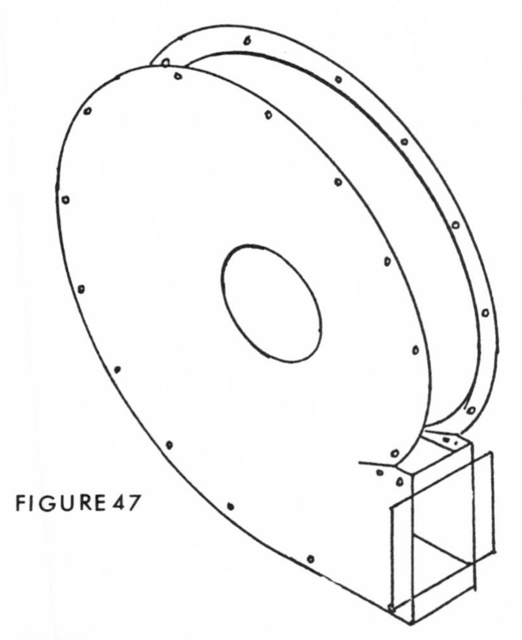

FIGURE 47

THE FAN ROTOR

8 radial vanes mounted on a sheet metal disc with blind rivets forms the fan rotor. 22 gauge metal is ideal for the both the disc and the vanes. Or you could use 22 gauge for the disc and as light as 26 gauge for the vanes. All of these parts must be carefully layed out and cut to shape to ensure that the rotor will be well balanced. Use only steel blind rivets or hammer set rivets to mount the vanes on the disc. Aluminum blind rivets may not be strong enough for safety in this application.

The entire layout of the disc is shown in figure 48. Using dividers, trammel, or an improvised trammel as described earlier, scribe three concentric circles of 3", 7" and 8" diameter. Divide into eight exactly equal segments and carefully punch the hole centers at the intersections. Cut out the disc precisely to the

8" diameter. Drill the 1/2" center hole as precisely as possible. It will be best to begin with a 1/8" pilot hole and gradually enlarge it with progressively larger bits. If you attempt to drill it with a 1/2" bit in one step it will almost surely run off center and ruin the disc. Drill sixteen 1/8" holes as indicated in figure 48.

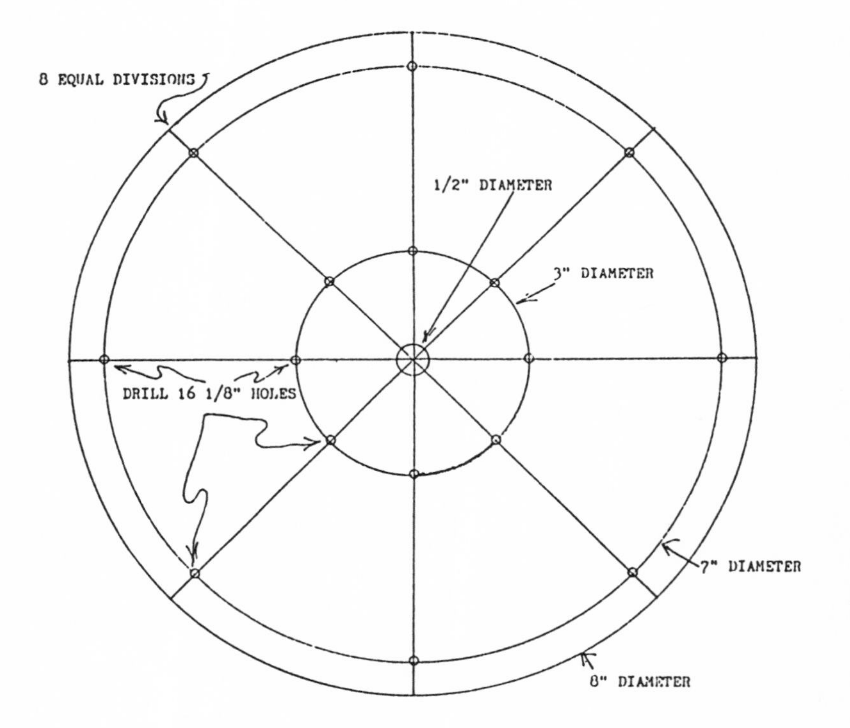

FIGURE 48

Lay out eight vanes as shown in figure 49 and cut them out carefully. Only one hole is drilled in each vane while a sharp center line for the second hole is scribed on the flange. Bend the flanges as in figure 50.

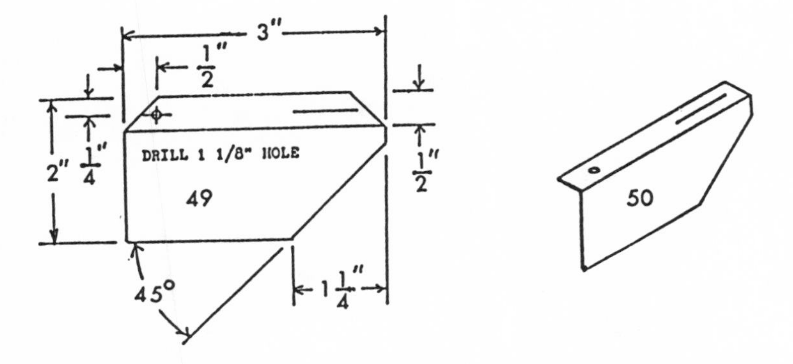

Each vane is installed with a single rivet and then the center line for the second hole is sighted through the hole in the disc as seen in figure 51. Clamp The flange securely with vise grip pliers to drill the second hole and install the second rivet. The completed rotor is seen installed on the arbor in figure 52.

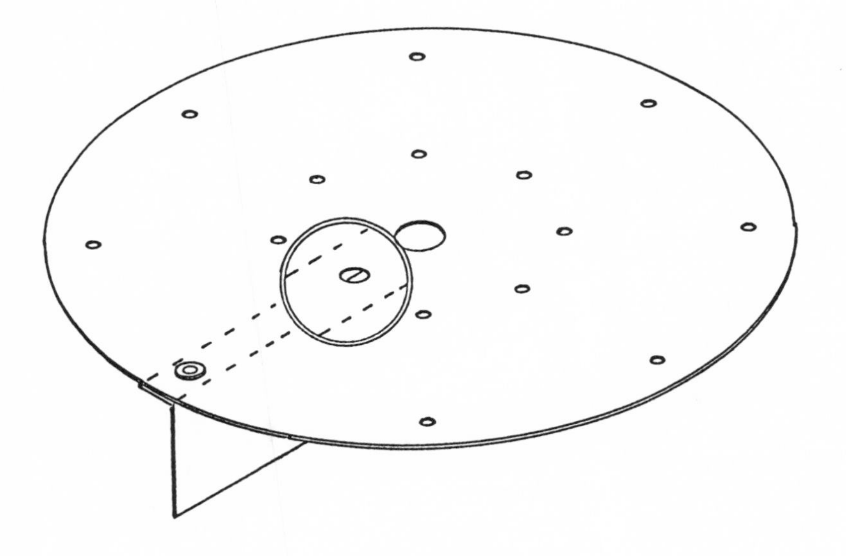

FIGURE 51

FIGURE 52

If all of the work is done carefully the rotor will be well ballanced. If there is a vibration problem when you run the fan you must definitely balance the rotor or build another more carefully. This fan will run at 3450 RPM and could eventually fly apart if it is run out of balance.

THE STAND

This simple weldment supports the fan/burner assembly with its motor/belt drive. All of the members except the lower brace are 1" X 1/8" angle iron. The lower brace is 1" X 1/8" strap iron. The dimensions are shown in figure 53. The angular view in figure 54 shows how the center member is cut and re-joined to provide convenient mounting for both the motor base and the arbor pillow blocks.

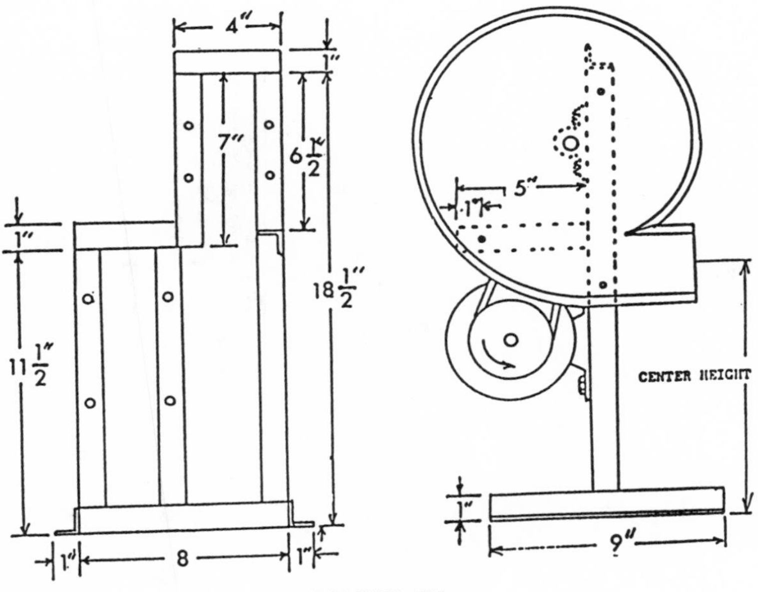

FIGURE 53

The location of the mounting holes for the arbor pillow blocks and the motor base are not given because there will be differences in finished heights of burner inlets and fan housing dimensions. Measure the center height of the burner inlet on the assembled furnace, dimension "A" in figure 55, and clamp the fan housing to the stand so that its outlet center is at that height. Dimension "B" in figure 55 is the distance from the outlet center to the working center of the fan. The sum of these dimensions will give you the center location for the arbor. When the arbor has been installed mount the fan housing to the stand with three machine screws through the back scroll as shown in figure 55. Hex nuts one size larger than the mounting screws will serve as spacing collars. The only requirement for the motor base mounting is that there be room to adjust belt tension.

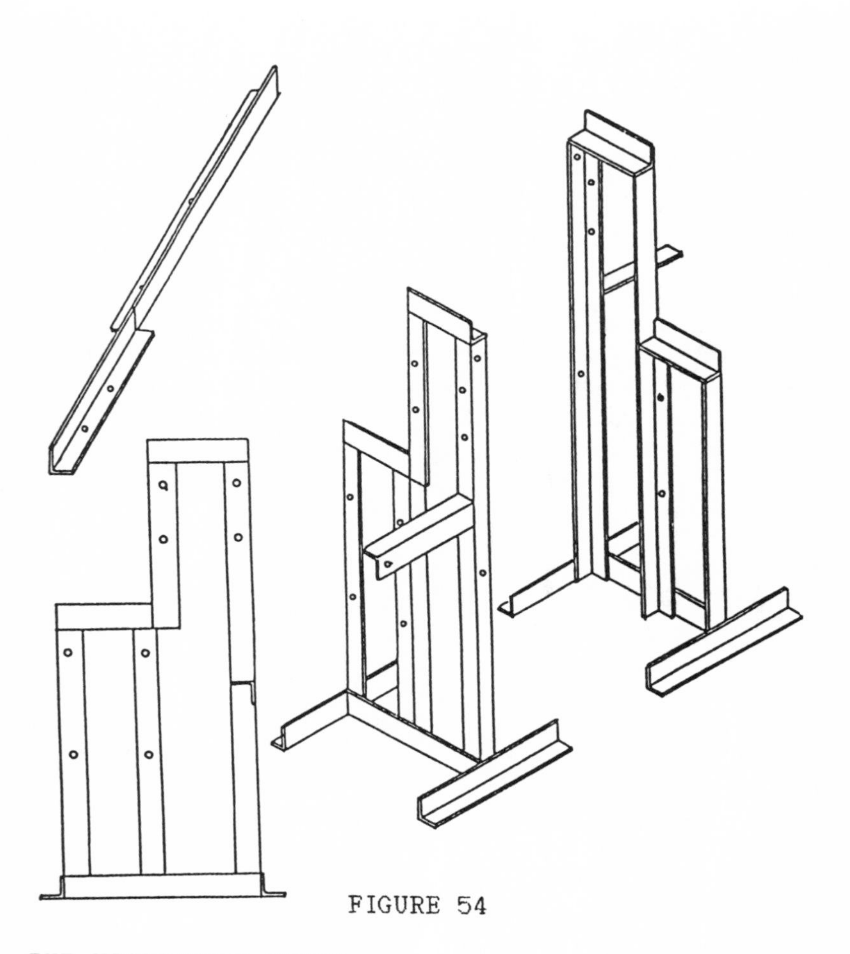

FIGURE 54

THE MOTOR/BELT DRIVE

The use of a threaded mandrel, or arbor, for mounting the fan rotor eliminates the need for a hub on the rotor. The flanges and nut that are normally used to mount a saw blade or buffing wheel will clamp the fan rotor nicely and that greatly reduces the labor of making the rotor. Any arbor of a physical size that will fit can be used. The configuration and rotation of this fan requires a right hand thread to mount the rotor. Of course if the configuration and rotation are reversed a left hand thread would be used. I selected a model

550 "Grinding/Buffing" mandrel made by Chicago Die Casting Co., 9148 King St., Franklin Park, IL 60131. It is available at Ace Hardware or True Value Hardware stores. If it is not in stock they can order it for you. Or you can order direct from Chicago Die Casting if there is not a dealer near you.

The mandrel is threaded at both ends, one right hand and the other left hand. It comes complete with two pillow block bearings, two thrust collars, flanges and nuts for both ends and a two step pulley, which I replaced with a 1 3/4" single step pulley. In addition to the mandrel a pair of 5/8" fiber thrust washers are needed.

The arrangement of the parts and the mounting is shown in figure 55. Since the mandrel is made to mount on a horizontal surface the oil holes are in the wrong location. I drilled a 3/32" hole in each pillow block and countersunk it with a 1/4" bit to provide oil holes for the vertical mounting. The fiber thrust washers are a very important item for without them the fan will be very noisy. The thrust collars are mounted on either side of the left hand pillow block to permit the mandrel pulley to fall in line with the motor pulley. When the final position of all parts is determined it will be neccessary to grind or file a flat area on the shaft for the set screws to seat against. This is very important because the set screws raise a burr on the shaft that will damage the bearings any time the mandrel is disassembled.

The motor mounting holes are located to mount the motor so that a pulley mounted on its shaft will fall in line with the mandrel pulley, and so that there is room for vertical adjustment. The slotted holes usually found in the motor base will allow enough movement for belt tension adjustment.

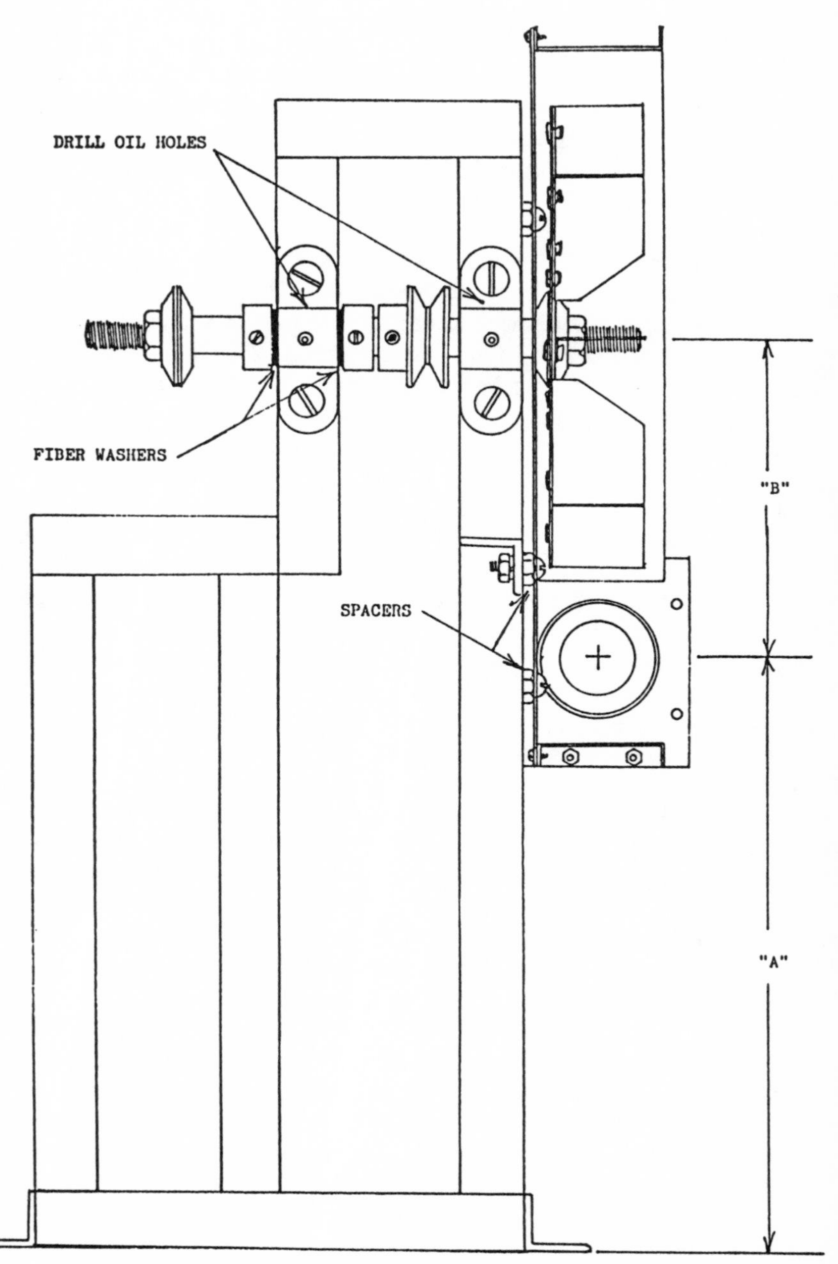

FIGURE 55

Having a 1725 RPM motor on hand, I used a 3 1/4" motor pulley to drive the 1 3/4" mandrel pulley at 3450 RPM. If a different speed motor is used you can determine the proper pulley size by simple calculation: Multiply the desired speed of the mandrel in RPM (revolutions per minute) by the pitch diameter of the mandrel pulley. Then divide the product by the speed in RPM of the motor on hand to learn the correct pitch diameter of the motor pulley. Remember that the pitch diameter of "A" pulleys is generally 1/4" less than the nominal outside diameter. Thus the pitch diameter of the 1 3/4" mandrel pulley is 1 1/2" and that of the 3 1/4" motor pulley is 3". The ratio is two to one.

And so 3450 RPM X 1 1/2" = 5175. And 5175/1725= 3"

For example perhaps you have a 1075 RPM motor on hand. If the direction of rotation is correct (counter-clock-wise as you face the shaft end) and it is 1/8 hp or better it should work OK. If the rotation is not reversible by changing the wire connections perhaps it will be possible to disassemble and reassemble the motor with the shaft out the opposite end.

So 3450 RPM X 1 1/2" = 5175. And 5175/1075 = 4.8" (approximately). Now a 5" "A" pulley has a pitch diameter of 4.75" and that's close enough.

The size of the belt is found by measuring the total distance over both pulleys as diagrammed in figure 56.

The completed motor/belt drive is shown in figure 57. When all is complete you should fashion a sheet metal cover for the belt and pulleys so that it will be impossible for anyone to get in contact with them while it is running. The belt drive will not be visible to one manipulating the gas valve or air shutter and there is a definite danger of injury here.

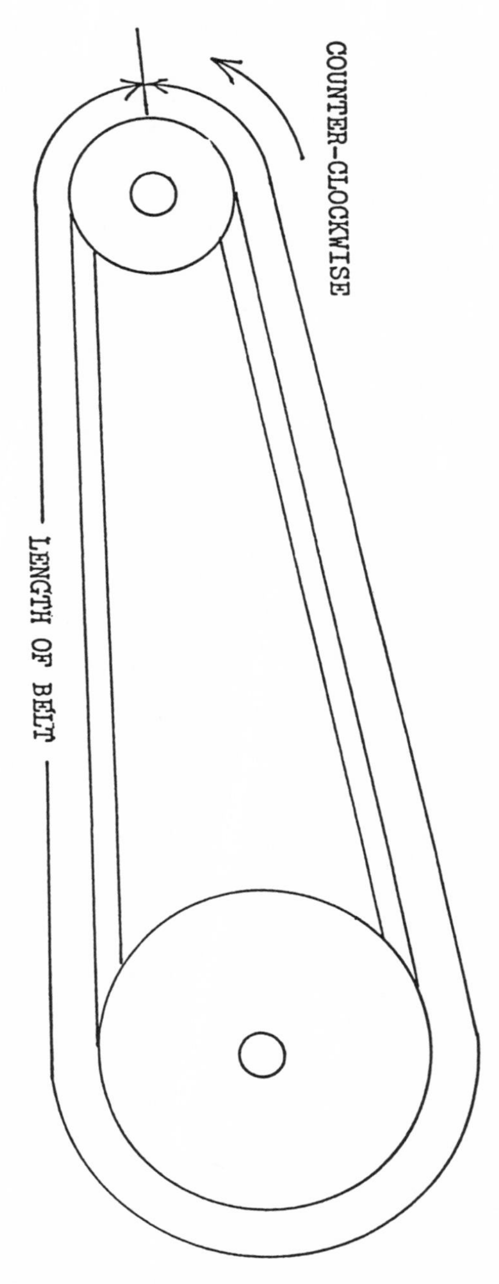

FIGURE 56

FIGURE 57

THE AIR INLET

In order to vary the size of the fire both the volume of gas and the volume of air must be adjustable. A duct is installed on the inlet cover which will reinforce the cover and, more important, establish some distance from the fan rotor to protect the operators fingers. The air inlet shutter is installed on the duct.

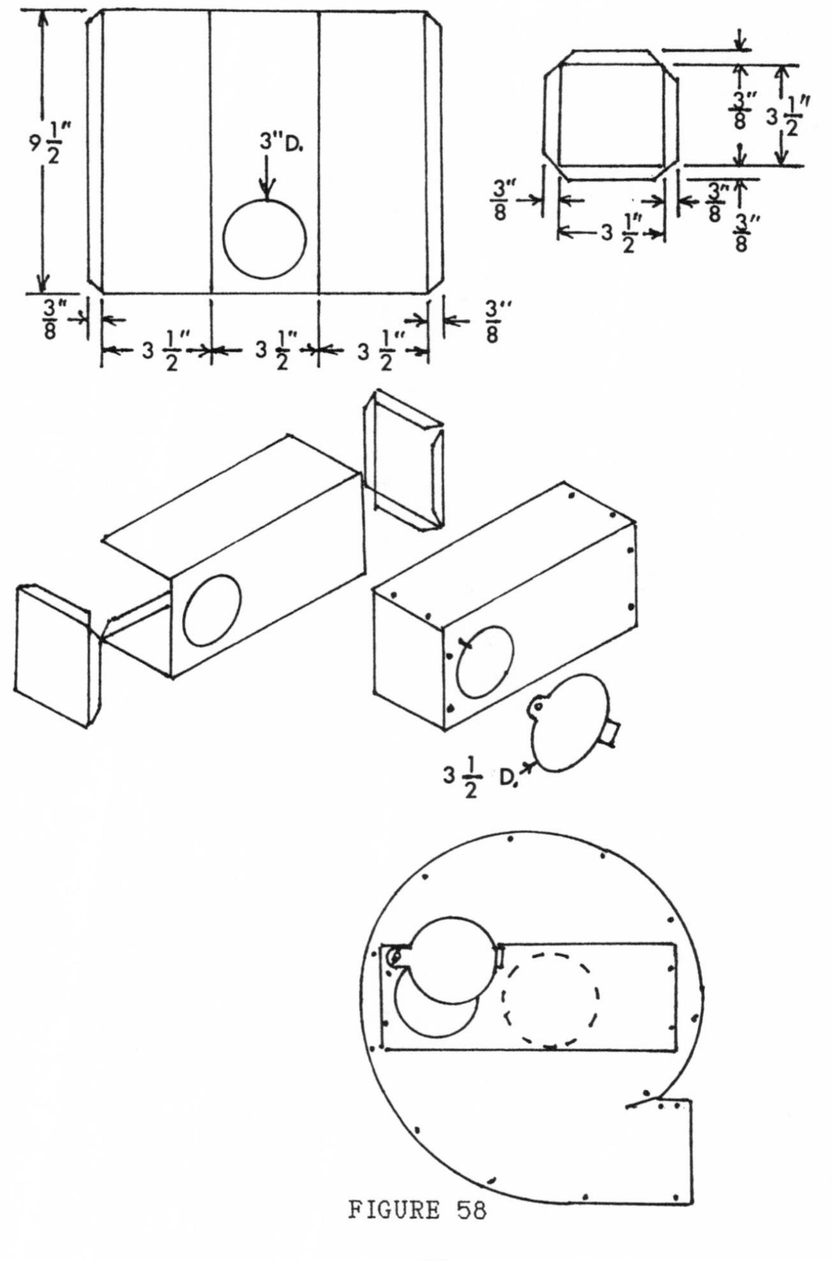

FIGURE 58

The dimensions and construction detail for the duct and shutter are shown in figure 58. 26 gauge metal is heavy enough for all of its parts. The ends of the duct can be installed with blind rivets. It is not neccessary to make the joints absolutely air tight but it should be neatly done for appearance and no sharp cutting edges should be exposed. The shutter has an ear with a 3/16" hole for the pivot and a tab opposite the ear that is bent up double to form a handle to manipulate it. Install a 3/16" machine screw in the duct for the shutter pivot and solder its head on the inside of the duct. Use a flat washer over a compression spring to apply tension to the shutter pivot and use a 3/16" wing nut to adjust the tension. Mount the completed duct on the front scroll of the fan housing with blind rivets. The heads of the blind rivets are thin and they will not interfere with the fan rotor. Figure 59 shows the burner complete with the duct and shutter.

FIGURE 59

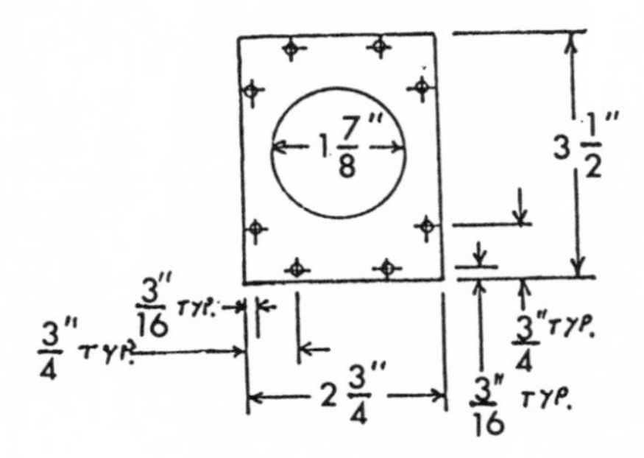

FIGURE 60

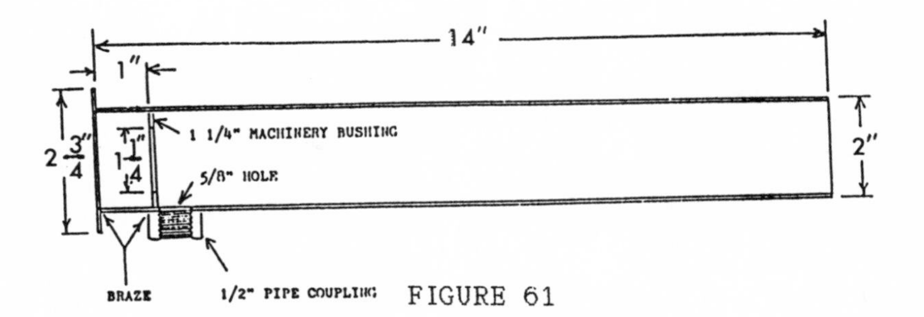

FIGURE 61

THE DELIVERY TUBE AND MIXING CHAMBER

Standard 2" automotive exhaust pipe tubing has an inside diameter of 1 7/8". A standard 1 1/4" machinery bushing, which looks like a large flat washer, is about 1/16" thick and has an outside diameter of 1 7/8". It will fit snugly inside the exhaust tubing and its 1 1/4" hole forms an ideal orfice to create a partial vacuum at the gas inlet. Most muffler shops regard a 14" length of 2" tubing as waste and they will let you have it at little or no cost. The machinery bushing is available at industrial supply, farm supply and some hardwares. In addition to these you need a 1/2" pipe coupling which is cut in half with a hacksaw.

Cut a piece of metal about 1/16" thick to neatly fit over the flanges of the fan outlet. This will be about 2 3/4" X 3 1/2". Cut a 1 7/8" diameter hole in its center. Center punch eight locations for holes to join the plate to the flanges of the fan outlet as shown in figure 60. Clamp the plate to the flanges and drill eight 3/16" holes through both members. Do not install the plate at this time.

Force the machinery bushing 1" inside the end of the burner delivery tube as shown in figure 61 and braze it in this position. Cut a 5/8" diameter hole in the tube against the downstream side of the machinery bushing and braze one half of a 1/2" pipe coupling over the hole. Make sure the correct end of the coupling is exposed so that it will accept the gas piping. Braze the prepared plate to the end of the tube to complete the delivery tube and mixing chamber assembly. Mount the assembly to the fan discharge with eight 3/16" machine screws with nuts and lock washers.

INSTALLING THE BURNER

The completed burner is shown installed in figure 62. The delivery tube is inserted in the inlet of the base and the space around the tube is packed with refractory mix. The furnace radiates intense heat during use so it must be an adequate distance from any combustible wall. It will certainly not be safe to operate this unit on a wooden floor. A 2" layer of dry silica sand must be spread under the furnace and extend over the entire area where a pot of molten metal might be carried. The electrical supply should be suspended above the floor so that it won't be exposed to molten metal in the event of a spill. A large vented hood should be installed above the furnace to carry away the excess heat. Ample ventilation must be provided to replace combustion air and to carry off fumes.

FIGURE 62

CONVERTING TO PROPANE

If the burner is used with natural gas the full size of the 1/2" pipe can be used for the gas inlet. But if propane is used a reducing orfice must be installed in the gas inlet.

Simply make a plug of mild steel to slip into the end of a 1/2" short pipe nipple. Drill a 5/32" hole through the center of the plug and braze it into the end of the nipple as shown in figure 63.

The conversion nipple is installed at the gas inlet of the burner and all other connections will be the same as for natural gas.

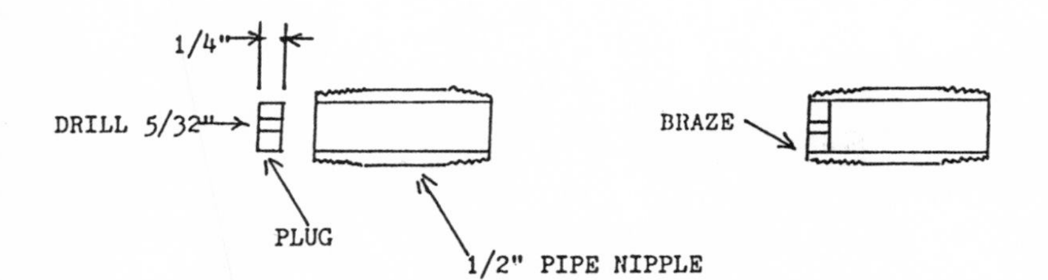

FIGURE 63

The burner consumes fuel at a high rate and so the small tanks as used for patio grills and camper outfits will not work. You need a 100 lb. tank of gas and a high delivery regulator to operate the furnace.

GAS PIPING

Although it can be operated without it, a gas solenoid valve should be installed at the gas inlet of the burner. These are available as a repair part from dealers in heating and air conditioning equipment. Immediately up stream from the solenoid valve should be the manual gas valve. The gas supply is then connected to the manual valve to complete the plumbing. Check all local codes and insurance regulations to ensure that your gas piping meets any and all requirements.

ELECTRICAL COMPONENTS

Mount a metal switch box on the fan housing and install a single pole switch to operate both the fan motor and the solenoid valve. That is: When the switch is "on" the solenoid opens and the fan motor runs. When the switch is "Off" the solenoid valve closes and the fan motor stops. It will be best to enclose the wiring at least from the solenoid valve to the switch in metal conduit, either flexible or rigid. Check all local codes and insurance regulations to ensure that your wiring meets any and all requirements.

LIGHTING THE FURNACE

A "lighting wand" can be made of stiff wire about 18" long. Bend a loop on one end and force in a bit of folded cloth for a wick. See figure 64. Dip the wick in kerosene or charcoal starting fluid. Be certain to cover the container and remove it an adequate distance from the furnace before you light it.

FIGURE 64

Raise the furnace central body with the lid closed. If you are ready to melt metal the charged crucible should be on the plinth with a couple of discs of cardboard under it to prevent fusing the pot and plinth together. With the air shutter completely closed and the manual gas valve completely closed turn on the switch. The fan will run and the solenoid will open but no gas will be delivered because the manual valve is closed. There will be a small amount of air delivered that will be sufficient for initial combustion. Light the wand and hold the flame over the combustion chamber where the air stream will disturb it but not extinguish it. With the other hand slowly open the manual gas valve until you get combustion. When the flame is large enough to support itself extinguish the wand and set it aside. Lower the furnace central body and gradually increase the size of the flame by opening the gas valve slowly and also slowly opening the air shutter. If the flame extinguishes at any time simply turn off the switch. Make certain that you also turn off the manual gas valve before you attempt to re-light the burner. Simply turn off the switch and close the manual gas valve when ever you want to shut down.

The optimum flame will be neutral or slightly carburizing, which means just a tiny bit short of oxygen. The opposite of a carburizing flame is an oxidizing flame, which has an excess of oxygen. A carburizing flame is luminous, which means it gives off light, while an oxidizing flame is non-luminous. These terms are rather ambiguous in the absence of an actual demonstration in full color and that is impossible in a book. It is easiest to learn to adjust the flame in a very dimly lit room so that you can distinguish between luminous and non-luminous. As you increase the amount of gas the flame will begin to escape at the vent in the lid. Then as you increase the amount of air it will retract into the furnace. When the gas valve is about 3/4 open the flame will escape at the vent regardless of the amount of air but it will change color. As you close the air shutter and reduce the air volume the flame will become more luminous as it turns yellow. As you open the shutter and admit more air the flame becomes less luminous as it turns blue. The perfect setting will be found between these two extremes and slightly towards the luminous. Keep in mind that fluxes and other elements carried in the flame can make it luminous even when there is an excess of oxygen. An excess of air reduces temperature, consumes metal in the pot and wastes heat by carrying it out the vent. You will most likely have to experiment over several melts to find the optimum setting for your burner.

CHAPTER V
CRUCIBLES AND TONGS

Metal must be melted in a container that has a melting point higher than itself. in the case of cast iron that means a ceramic crucible but some other metals and alloys can be melted in steel pots. Crucibles are made of a variety of materials but those commonly available are made of clay and graphite or silicon carbide. There are advantages and disadvantages to both and your selection will be determined by your most frequent usage more than any other factor.

CLAY/GRAPHITE CRUCIBLES

These, as the name implies are made of clay and graphite. Some are specially glazed to make them more durable. They are the cheaper of the two common types but not as strong as silicon carbide. There are also crucibles made of clay only that are yet cheaper. But they are rather too delicate for use in the home shop. Their primary use in this age is for metallurgical work.

Iron attacks silicon carbide crucibles and so clay/graphite is the better choice for melting iron on a continuing basis. On the other hand you can break a clay/graphite crucible in a single use while it takes rather a long time for the iron to consume the silicon carbide crucible. And so if you will melt only a small amount of iron occasionaly the picture changes.

A clay/graphite crucible must be "tempered" before its first use. That means it must be heated very gradually to a bright red heat and then allowed to cool slowly. Failure to do so may mean that the crucible will break in its first use. Thereafter it must be stored in a dry condition between uses. If it is ever allowed to absorb moisture from humid air it must be tempered again before use.

If properly cared for and handled gently it is possible to get 50 or more melts with a clay/graphite crucible. They are suitable for melting grey iron, brass bronze, aluminum and zinc alloys.

The general rules for handling a clay/graphite crucible are simple and direct:

1. Use properly fitting tongs.
2. Empty the crucible completely at the end of each use.
3. Return the crucible to the furnace after pouring to cool slowly.
4. Store in an air tight container when out of use for extended time.
5. Avoid over fluxing the melt.

As with all melting pots a separate crucible is reserved for each type of metal melted if you hope to control quality of your castings. Residue from previous melts can contaminate an alloy

SILICON CARBIDE CRUCIBLES

These are significantly stronger, especially when hot, than clay/graphite crucibles but also more costly. Their main advantage is that they will stand much abuse and so they are very forgiving in unskilled hands. They are impervious to moisture and so they don't have to be stored with special care. And they don't have to be tempered before the first use. While iron attacks them and gradually consumes them from the inside they are ideal for melting the copper alloys, brass and bronze. Even when handled abusively they will endure for a great many melts.

METAL POTS

Since each metal melted should have its own crucible an assortment for some shops might become very costly. Both aluminum and zinc alloys can be melted in a steel pot and they are quite cheaply made.

Simply weld a disc to the end of a short length of large diameter pipe and forge a pouring lip. Standard weight pipe or well casing is ideal. And the bottom should not be greatly heavier than the sides. While a heavy pot lasts longer it consumes excess fuel in use.

About the only objection to the use of steel pots is that the metal can become contaminated by iron picked up from the pot. This can be a serious problem, especially with aluminum, because it tends to make the metal gassy and thus porous castings result. A ceramic lining or glaze will reduce or eliminate the problem.

There are commercial glazes and washes made, but as in the case of most foundry supplies they are difficult or impossible for the home shop user to obtain. Fortunately the glaze suggested for the furnace lining in this manual is quite effective. It is also cheap and readily available. Simply apply it to the inside of the pot before each melt. It tends to break away as the pot cools and contracts so must be continually renewed.

You can also line the inside of the pot with castable refractory or the home-brewed refractory used to line the furnace. Add some ground glass to the mix to provide a durable glaze. While such a pot could never be used to melt iron it can serve nicely for melting brass.

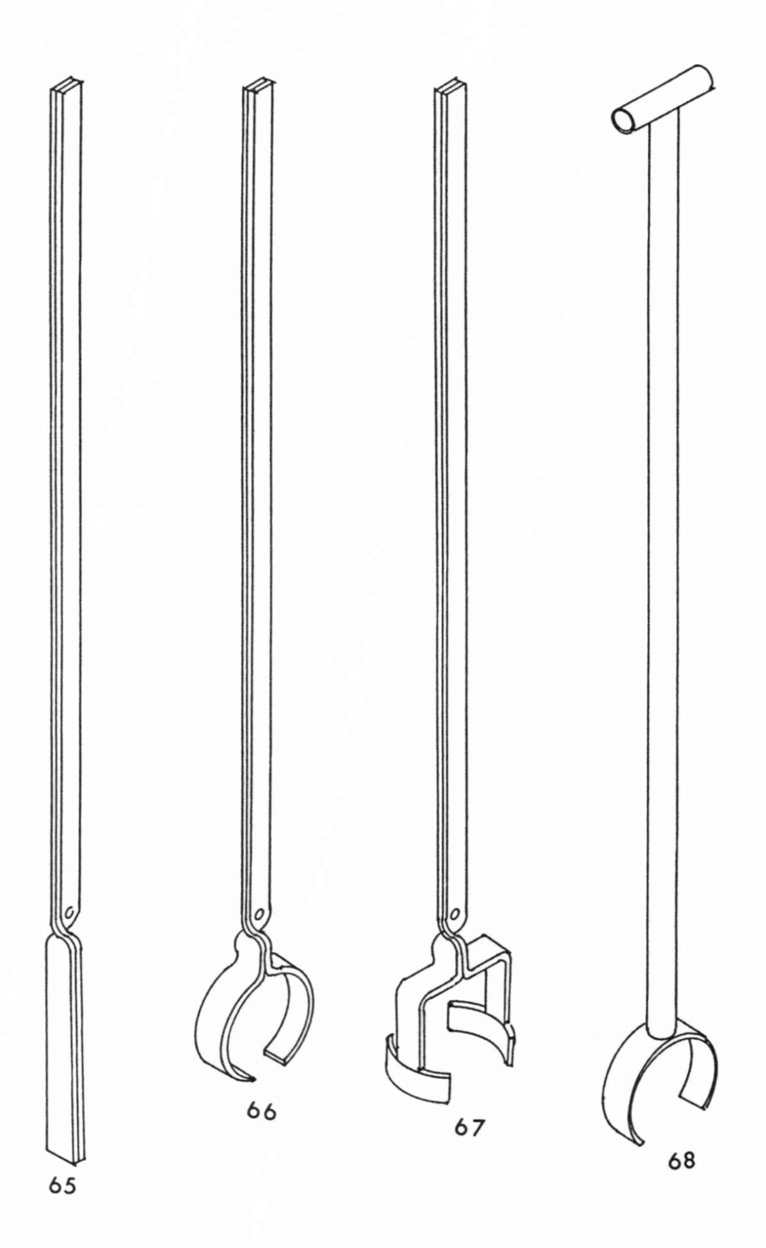
65
66
67
68

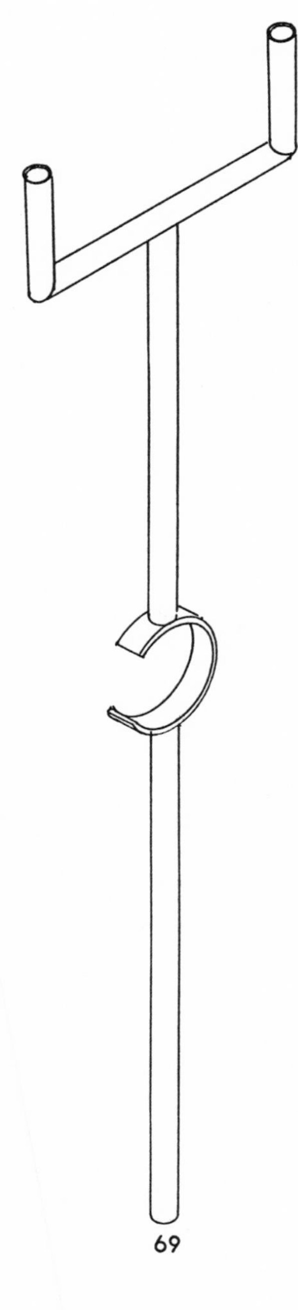
69

CRUCIBLE TONGS

Some means must be provided to remove the crucible of molten metal from the furnace. The usual practice is to lift out the crucible with tongs and transfer it to a pouring shank. My objection to the practice is that the crucible must come too close to the operator's mid section and it is suspended above his feet for a period of time. This seems a serious danger to me with any metal, but the radiant heat from a crucible of iron could ignite ordinary clothing at considerable distance. And this is to say nothing of the consequences if the crucible should break or slip from the tongs. There is also some time lost in transferring the crucible to the shank and additional danger of a spill during the transfer. And so I prefer to fashion my tongs to grip the crucible from the side to both remove it from the furnace and to pour the molds.

A side-gripping tongs is shown in figure 66 while the conventional "lift-out" tongs are shown in figure 67.

An alternate to the side-gripping tongs is an open ended shank as shown in figure 68. A two man version of the same concept is shown in figure 69. Note that only one of the two men can tip the crucible while the other can merely support half the weight. These shanks can be used to both remove the crucible from the furnace and to pour the molds. The advantage is that some distance is maintained between the operators and the molten metal. One disadvantage is that the crucible can easily slip from the ring near the end of the pour and so it requires extra skill to use them. They are illustrated in rudimentary form. A shank for a number 6 crucible could be made with 3/4" black iron pipe for a handle and a ring of 3/16" X 1" hot rolled steel as illustrated. But larger crucibles should have the ring reinforced so that it could not spread. All welding must be very sound and secure and they must be abusively tested with twice the weight you expect to pour before using them, regardless of the size.

Crucibles are smaller at the bottom than at the top and some styles are larger in the middle than at the top. The largest diameter portion is called the "bilge". The proper place to grip a crucible is from one third to one half the distance from the top to the bottom, or just below the bilge. The lift-out tongs in figure 67 are made so that they automatically grip the crucible at the correct area when the horizontal portion contacts the top. they are formed so that no pressure is applied to the rim, which would almost surely break the crucible. The curved gripping pads conform nicely to the crucible so that pressure is applied uniformly. A simple gauge can be added to the side-gripping tongs in figure 66 to provide the same conveneience.

It is not difficult to make crucible tongs but care must be taken to make them fit properly. In fact commercially made tongs must often be altered because crucibles are not all that uniform in size and shape. And so there are other good reasons to "custom build" your tongs besides avoiding a substantial expense.

3/16" X 3/4" hot rolled steel is adequate for crucibles up to a number 6 but 1/4" X 3/4" stock should be used for a number 8 crucible. Metal of this weight can be cold forged but it will require less force if you heat it to a bright red heat. The gas fired crucible furnace provides an adequate forge for the purpose.

Begin with two bars of 3/16" X 3/4" hot rolled steel 36" long. Drill a 5/16" about hole 7" from the end of each bar and join them with a 5/16" rivet. (A bolt and nut will not be reliable!)

Heat the area below the pivot to a bright red heat and clamp it in the vise about one inch below the pivot to give it a half twist with a wrench as shown in figure 65. This work must be done deftly before the metal cools so have the vise and wrench adjusted and ready before you heat the metal.

Now you have what might be used as a simple forge tongs. The gripping members can be shaped to many special purposes. One practical use for such a tongs is to add metal to a partly full crucible of molten metal. (Never drop it in!)

The next step is to bend the gripping members out sharply and then forge them to fit the curve of the crucible as in figure 66. I use scraps of large pipe as a form to forge my tongs. And then I use the pipe to make metal pots.

It will improve the tongs to bend an angle of one or two degrees near the pivot to reduce stooping during the pouring.

Make tongs to fit each size of crucible you use and never handle a crucible with improperly fitting tongs.

Metal pots should have stops welded on them so that they can't slip through the tongs.

Always have ingot molds or pig molds prepared into which you'll pour excess metal when the molds are filled. The metal must never be allowed to solidify in the crucible because it is likely to break it when it expands before re-melting. Yes, even a steel pot!

CHAPTER VI
OPERATING THE FURNACE

As mentioned at the outset there is rather more to producing metal castings than merely melting the metal. Certainly pattern making and molding are crafts in themselves, and each of these are divided into specialties too numerous to mention. And all of this is to say nothing of the metallurgy, chemistry and all of the administrative skills that go into the operation of a foundry. A tour of a modern foundry is awe inspiring and you would certainly come away feeling that these fascinating operations could never be reduced to the home shop level.

By contrast the giant church bells of three and four centuries ago were all cast with none of the technology that serves so well in our age. The bell caster could carry the tools of his trade in a single pouch. (But more likely his apprentice carried them when they moved to a new job.) He would contract to cast a new bell or to re-cast a broken one. Then he would procure all of the needed materials and supplies and set about the task hiring local labor, which was certainly unskilled, and beasts of burden to do the heavy manual work.

A furnace would be built right on the site with local stone and clay. And the pit for the mold was dug at the base of the furnace. Ramps, cranes and derricks were erected. The mold was made in the pit by the most ingenious use of sweeps. Somehow the huge cope was lifted off and replaced as required. It was all a very major undertaking, for an entire foundry was being set up, usually for a single job.

When all was ready the furnace was charged and lit. The draft might have been furnished by bellows or natural winds. Without a single electronic device the bell caster knew at what moment to give the order to punch out the bot and let the molten metal run into the mold to cast a bell of sometimes many tons. Then it was neccessary to begin almost immediately to dig down to be prepared to raise the casting from the drag at the correct moment so that it would not break as it contracted on the core upon cooling.

The entire operation took a great deal of time and required many strong backs and willing hands. But it was the accumulated knowledge of the bell caster that made it all possible. And so it is for the aspiring amateur fondryman of today to acquire the neccessary knowledge and skill to produce the castings we need in the home shop. The melting of the metal might be compared to heating water to make soup: You simply let it get hot enough! But as in making soup there are other ingredients and considerations. Most of the modern devices are as unavailable in the home shop as they were to the bell caster of centuries ago. And every bit of our really useful knowledge and skill must be wrung out of our personal experience like the bell casters apprentice.

And so to melt metal and pour it into a mold is the best way to begin to learn. Each experience will teach you something of what you need to know to do it better the next time, and you will gradually acquire the knowledge and skill you need. There really is no short cut. I see no reason why we could not learn to cast a giant church bell if we really wanted to. So surely the small things we want to cast will be easy by comparison. There are a few things you should know before you melt and pour for the first time.

SETTING UP THE FOUNDRY

Eventual success of your casting plans is a certainty and so your primary concern from the very first moment must be for safety. The consequences of carelessness in the foundry are so grim that you simply must never relax your vigil. Do all of your work with SAFETY foremost in your mind.

Fire is the obvious first danger so install your furnace at a good distance from any combustible surface. This means at least two or three feet from walls and partitions. Of course it can't be installed on a combustible floor because it vents partially through the safety hole in the base. A bed of sand at least 2" thick is absolutely neccessary under the furnace to catch a spill in the event a crucible breaks or tips over in the furnace. And the sand is sloped so that molten metal can't run to a combustible wall. A vented sheet metal hood over the furnace will carry out excess heat.

Certainly no flammable liquids or fuel tanks should be any where near the furnace. If you fire your furnace with propane the tank should be ouside the building.

Gas piping must be strong enough to withstand any blow it might recieve during operation. I suggest only threaded black iron pipe. Plastic or rubber tubing is certainly not safe and neither is a flexible appliance connector.

Electrical wiring must be kept off the floor where a spill of molten metal might run over it. And it must be a good distance from the radiant heat of the furnace.

You must survey your set up to make certain there is no possible chance for a fire to start. And you must have means at hand to extinguish a fire in case you have overlooked something.

Explosion is the next danger to be considered. Though not as likely as fire the results can be more disastrous immediately. And it is not only the gas/air mixture that can explode. The greater danger is in the event of a spill of molten metal on concrete, or water somehow getting into molten metal. The steam that builds up rapidly can blow great chunks out of a concrete floor that does not even seem damp. For this reason all of your melting and pouring should be done over a bed of dry silica sand at least 2" thick. And you should never carry a crucible of molten metal beyond the sand bed. Even a single drop of water in a crucible of molten metal will cause a bad spatter. And a cold chunk of metal added to a molten pot can cause a violent explosion.

Aerosol spray cans and propane torches are items you might overlook. These can become hot enough to burst if stored near the furnace.

Ventilation is very important. First to carry away excess heat and to replace combusition air. And there will always be hazardous fumes, if only carbon-monoxide. A large sheet metal hood over the furnace with a substantial pipe leading outside is the best idea.

Everything must be in good working condition and the working area must be clear of all obstacles. When you melt you must plan the whole operation and rehearse your sequence of operation to make sure you can carry it out with what is at hand. A clear retreat path must be part of the plan so make sure there is nothing to stumble over. In general all of your moves should be forward steps but you must allow for error and emergency. A mold can run out at the parting or other mishaps can occur.

It is unlikely that most home shop operators will feel able to afford many of the personal protection devices or clothing items. But a minimum should include a full transparent face shield, protective gloves or mitts with long gauntlets and a full length protective apron. Substantial shoes must be worn. The foundry is no place for sneakers or sandals. Every possible precaution must be taken to avoid injury from spatters and spills of molten metal and from the intense radiant heat.

With a well set up foundry and a mold waiting to be poured you are ready for your first melt but you should know something about the metal you will pour before you melt it. You will be wise to begin with the lower temperature metals as you acquire your foundry skills.

ZINC ALLOYS

These include what is commonly called "white metal" or "pot metal". A well known proprietary version is called ZAMAC, which is an alloy of zinc, aluminum, magnesium, antimony and copper. These alloys are used to make die-castings of countless items from toys to machinery parts. The pillow blocks, pulleys and thrust collars of the fan mandrel are zinc alloy die castings. It is also an excellent material for sand castings and ideal to learn with because it melts at a bit over 700 degrees F. and pours nicely at from 800 to 900 degrees. It is very cheap and easily available. The castings are strong, easily machined and they do not rust.

Zinc does not begin to vaporize until something beyond 1600 degrees F. but it is quite often found plated with chrome or cadmium and these give off harmful vapors when heated. You must always be very cautious of fumes and vapors in the foundry.

These alloys can be melted in a steel pot without flux. But a little borax may help if the scrap is dirty. The impurities will form a granular dross and rise to the surface of the molten metal where they are easily skimmed off with a heavy weight steel spoon before pouring.

ALUMINUM ALLOYS

These resemble zinc alloy in appearance but they are much lighter in weight. Automotive pistons are probably the best all around material for home shop use but practically any form of aluminum is OK for casting. Extrusions and cooking utensils are nearly pure aluminum and their casting quality can be improved by adding a small amount of zinc alloy. Some lawn mower housings and much aircraft salvage has a high magnesium content and it will ignite and burn with intense heat when you melt it. You can extinguish it only by covering it with dry sand and it must be discarded as useless for casting in the home shop. Beverage cans are a poor choice because there is great loss in melting them. It is not safe to crush the cans into a briquette and plunge it into a pot of molten metal because trapped moisture can cause a violent explosion. Castings are bright, durable and rust free. Pouring temperature is from 1200 to 1400 degrees F. It can be melted in a steel pot without flux. The dross is easily skimmed as with zinc alloy. But the metal will begin to deteriorate after frequent re-melting so you should use up all sprues and risers promptly and avoid melting too great an excess for each session.

COPPER ALLOYS

Pure copper and of course brass and bronze can be used to cast many useful items for the shop. Brass is often acceptable in place of iron when aluminum or zinc alloy just won't do. All of these are poured at something in excess of 2000 degrees F. and so they are more difficult and dangerous to handle. It is best to melt them in a ceramic crucible but it can be done in a lined steel pot.

Flux of some sort is generally neccessary. Borax is cheap, effective and commonly available. Use it sparingly for it tends to consume the crucible. Phosphor-copper is used as a deoxidant but that can be difficult for the home shop operator to purchase in the shot form used in foundries. But it is sold by welding supplies in stick or rod form for welding copper pipe. The grade without silver is the one you want. As with zinc alloys and aluminum the dross can be skimmed with a heavy steel spoon.

There is a danger of zinc poisoning when melting brass because it is poured at a temperature above the vaporizing temperature of the zinc. The traditional remedy for zinc poisoning is to eat ice cream and drink lots of milk. But it is not a frivolous matter and every precaution should be taken to avoid inhaling the vapors. That means adequate ventilation, minimum pouring temperature and minimum exposure. Of course there are other hazardous vapors as well so caution will be rewarded.

There are special rules for gating and pouring brass molds and the copper alloys are notably more difficult to cast than zinc alloys or aluminum. And because of the higher pouring temperature wet molds are more likely to blow up. A full transparent face shield should be considered a must.

GREY IRON

Probably the cheapest and best material for casting at the commercial level. It is certainly easier and more economical to melt by the ton than it is by the pound. But few of us need iron castings of great weight, even if we could manage to pour them. And 20 pounds of the white hot stuff in a crucible might very well make you wonder why you thought you wanted to melt it in the first place! But there are ever fewer sources for grey iron castings for home shop projects and so we will have to cast them ourselves if we are persuaded that we must have them. Those that we cast will be had only after considerable study and labor. Grey iron should definitely not be the first metal you cast on your own.

It pours at somewhere between 2600 and 2800 degrees F. and that is dazzling white heat. It will take 45 minutes or more to melt in the gas furnace. I suggest no larger than a number 4 crucible for your earliest melts. And I suggest that you "train" for the project with a reliable, serious minded and congenial partner While one man can do it alone it is much easier to have an extra pair of hands. But the foundry is no place for idle bystanders who may distract you at a critical moment with questions or, worse, make unwise moves out of ignorance while intending to help. Molten iron is very dangerous to handle. For instance a simple thing like cooling a rod in a bucket of water and then using it for a "slag dam" while pouring can cause a violent explosion that will throw molten iron all over the place.

The most persistent problem with iron is slag inclusion. And the other serious challenge is to produce castings that are soft enough to machine. You should certainly expect some failures in your early experience. But all of the problems can be overcome if you take your inspiration from the bell caster.

FLUXING

Flux is used in melting metals to separate the impurities and bring them to the top of the melt for removal. A small amount of limestone is used with iron. Crushed limestone from the quarry or agriculatural lime from the farm supply works well. Oyster shells as used for poultry grit is OK too.

Any form of pure limestone but not combinations like plaster of paris because it contains sulphur. (Bad for iron!) A small amount means up to 2% of the metal weight. That's about 4 to 6 ounces in a 20 pound charge or half that amount in a number 4 crucible. The flux is added to the cold crucible when it is charged with iron.

HARDNESS CONTROL

Many factors effect the ultimate hardness of a casting but there are only a few over which we have any control in the home shop. The main factors are carbon and silicon content and the rate of cooling after pouring. We can do something about these. And we can begin with nice soft iron scrap in the first place, since There is little hope that we could make soft iron out of hard iron. I'll leave it to others to explain the mysteries of metallurgy and cast iron chemistry, but I'll try to tell you what you can do about it.

Carbon and silicon are inter-related in the alloying of iron. Each effects the other in the way they are combined in the iron and that along with the rate of cooling effects the ultimate hardness. Ferro-silicon can be added to iron in cupola practice but it is generally used as an "inoculant" in the sprue when the iron is melted in a crucible. The product is nearly impossible for most home shop operators to buy so we may as well forget it. What you can do is to begin with nice soft iron and protect it from excessive change in silicon and carbon content while melting. We simply mix the iron, which is broken up into nuggets, with some form of pure carbon. This can be granulated charcoal or coke. The carbon occupies the spaces between the iron and somehow retards the change of silicon and carbon content in the iron. Enough said! I don't understand it either but it works. You can mix the limestone and carbon together to distribute it nicely among the nuggets of iron. It will all rise to the top by the end of the melt. It is additionaly helpful to cover the crucible during the melt. You can make a cover of castable refractory. More about hardness later.

"SLAGGING THE POT"

Having separated the impurities so that they can raise to the top of the pot we must now remove it. With the cooler melting metals it's a simple matter to skim the granular dross. The small amount that remains is easily pushed back from the pouring lip and gives no trouble. But the temperature of iron is so high that the impurities become semi-fluid and form a thick sticky mass called slag. The limestone flux reduces the melting point of the slag to make it more fluid but it is still nasty stuff. The pot radiates an intense heat and it is very difficult to approach it to remove the slag. If you pour without "slagging the pot" some of it will enter the mold and ruin the casting so the job simply must be done. The process requires advance planning and some simple equipment.

Begin with a cold crucible and charge it with iron nuggets, carbon and flux. Don't wedge pieces in the pot because they will expand before melting and may break it. Get prepared to "slag the pot" before you begin to melt.

The only practical means you have to do the job in the home shop is to scrape it off the top, and to do this you must tip the crucible so that the molten metal is nearly at the rim. You can't pour off the slag because the iron will slip under it and carry gobs of the nasty stuff along. So you take a dry oak stick about three feet long and scrape the slag off the top of the tilted pot. The wood will burn of course but you can shove it into the sand to smother the fire when you are done. DON'T plunge it in water! Of course all of this work is done over the dry sand bed.

To both tip the pot and skim it is too much for one man unless you have a fixture to hold the pot at the required angle as you skim it. You can easily devise an adjustable fixture made of angle iron and strap iron. But simpler yet is to prepare a mound of dry sand with a brick fixed to hold the pot at the right angle as it rests against the sand mound. Then you set the crucible of molten iron on the brick, deftly scrape the slag over the rim and onto the dry sand with your oak stick and pick up the pot with the tongs to pour the mold. An additional few moments will be saved if you have a support prepared to hold the tongs in position as you slag the pot.

Rehearse all of this a number of times to get it well fixed in your mind. Prepare adequate ingot molds or pig molds before you melt. You can simply mold an assortment of moderate to large sized dowels about a foot long to cast lathe turning stock with your excess metal.

When all is in readiness you can put the crucible in the furnace with a couple discs of cardboard on the plinth to prevent them from fusing together. Then light the furnace, adjust to a near neutral flame and be prepared to wait 45 minutes or more. About the only temperature gauge you will have will be the dazzling whiteness of the molten metal. Of course the furnace lining will be white hot some time before the iron is ready. After 45 minutes you can lift the lid from the pot with tongs and push the slag aside for a moment with the oak stick to attempt to judge the iron. Of course the burner must be shut down to enter the furnace, but you can re-light it if neccessary. You are flying by the seat of your pants from this moment because that's all the help I can offer on melting and pouring iron.

SOFTENING HARD CASTINGS

You can't very well change the composition of iron once it is cast. But one of the factors that causes hardness is "chilling", which means to cool it too fast. For that reason it is best to leave iron castings in the mold as long as you can possibly stand to wait. Over night is not too long for larger castings. But small ones will cool quite fast in the mold. If the castings are too hard to be machined due to rapid cooling they can be annealed by heat treatment.

Prepare a steel pot from large pipe as for a melting pot and provide a steel cover of about the same thickness metal with a 1/2" hole drilled in the center. The lid should contact the rim of the pot nicely.

Prepare a bundle of steel or iron wires long enough to rest on the bottom of the pot and protrude about an inch through the hole in the lid. Old coat hangers work nicely.

Pack the castings in the pot with enough pulverized charcoal or coke to surround them to a thickness of at least two inches and place the cover on the pot.

Insert the bundle of wires through the hole so that they are imbedded in the center of the charcoal.

The procedure is to raise the temperature of the castings to a bright red heat and hold the temperature for about a half hour. Then the entire pot is burried in dry ashes to cool slowly for at least over night. The wires are used to check the temperature in the center of the pot, for the outside can be very hot while the center is not. Simply pull out one wire when you think it might be hot enough. If the portion that was burried in the charcoal is bright red you can begin to time it. If not you pull another wire after waiting for the temperature to come up. There is no danger of treating it too long if the carbon does not burn away. Keep in mind that you will be generating carbon monoxide with this operation so be very certain of your ventilation.

RULES FOR ALL METALS

Each metal has its peculiarities that must be learned as you use them but all of them deserve a basic respect. These rules are in the interest of safety.

1. Use only sound crucibles. A cracked pot is on the verge of breaking.

2. Use only properly fitting tongs.

3. Don't try to handle a crucible brim full of metal.

4. Pre-heat metal that is to be added to a pot of molten metal. You can set it on the furnace lid near the vent or hold it over the vent with tongs. Plunging cold metal into a pot can cause a violent explosion.

5. Use tongs to gently add metal to a pot. Never drop it in.

6. Add only moderate amounts of metal to a pot to avoid chilling the melt.

7. Examine all of your scrap piece by piece. A coffee can of small scrap could contain something dangerous.

8. Make sure there is no trapped liquid in any scrap that is added to a pot of molten metal.

9. Don't cool skimmers, stirring rods or tongs in water. A wet tool in contact with molten metal is very dangerous.

10. Always have ample ingots or pig molds to dispose of all the metal you melt in case a mold fails.

These comments by no means cover even a fraction of what you'll need to know, but you have the place to begin to learn. I urge you to read as many books as you can find on foundry work. But it is even more important to be very alert in all of your shop activity. It is a fact that the answers to problems usually lie within the problems themselves. Though often elusive the answers will reveal themselves to you if you are dilligent and persistent. Generations of craftsmen have discovered and re-discovered the answers for centuries, and that is the major part of the joy of craftsmanship. Although it is true that you lack most of the technical aids of the modern metal casting industry you do have much more at your disposal than our friend and ancestor, the bell caster.

Best wishes for success in all of your shop projects.

END